THE STRANGE LIVES
OF FAMILIAR INSECTS

OTHER BOOKS BY EDWIN WAY TEALE

GRASSROOT JUNGLES

NEAR HORIZONS

THE GOLDEN THRONG

INSECT FRIENDS

THE JUNIOR BOOK OF INSECTS

DUNE BOY

THE LOST WOODS

DAYS WITHOUT TIME

CIRCLE OF THE SEASONS

NORTH WITH THE SPRING

AUTUMN ACROSS AMERICA

JOURNEY INTO SUMMER

ADVENTURES IN NATURE

THE LOST DOG

THE STRANGE LIVES

WITH PHOTOGRAPHS BY THE AUTHOR
AND DRAWINGS BY SU ZAN SWAIN

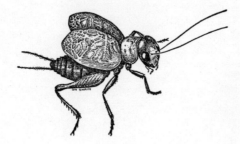

OF FAMILIAR INSECTS

EDWIN WAY TEALE

DODD, MEAD & COMPANY   NEW YORK   1962

$$\frac{595.7}{I}$$

DEDICATED TO

J. HENRI FABRE

WHOSE BOOKS OPENED THE
DOOR TO POPULAR INTEREST
IN THE LIVING INSECTS

FOREWORD

I REMEMBER once walking in the country with a man who seemed interested only in names. Our conversation ran something like this:

"What's that?"

"A woolly bear caterpillar."

"Oh."

"What's that?"

"A black swallowtail butterfly."

"Oh."

"What's that?"

"An orb spider."

"Oh."

Each time the light of curiosity went out of his eyes, his interest died, as soon as he heard the name. The name was all that mattered to him. He had no desire to know anything about the thing named. All the fascination of the living outdoors, the amazing activity of plant and animal existence, meant nothing to him.

This book is written to stimulate a different and a higher kind of interest. It goes beyond the name. It is written for those who are interested in the living creatures that would be as fascinating by any other name. It is an exploration among the most bizarre and astonishing of all the animals, dwellers in the familiar, often overlooked realm of the insects.

FOREWORD

I am indebted to the United States Department of Agriculture for permission to use as Part I of this book a contribution originally made to *Insects, The Yearbook of Agriculture, 1952*. One of the life-histories, that of the lacewing fly, appeared, prior to book publication, in *Audubon Magazine*. I wish to express my appreciation to the editor and to the National Audubon Society for permission to include it here.

EDWIN WAY TEALE

Trail Wood,
Hampton, Connecticut

CONTENTS

FOREWORD   ix

PART I. THE STRANGENESS OF INSECT LIFE   1

PART II. WHAT LIFE IS LIKE FOR AN INSECT   15

PART III. LIVES OF FAMILIAR INSECTS

    1. THE LIFE OF THE MAY FLY   63
    2. THE LIFE OF THE DRAGONFLY   74
    3. THE LIFE OF THE TERMITE   85
    4. THE LIFE OF THE CRICKET   94
    5. THE LIFE OF THE PRAYING MANTIS   101
    6. THE LIFE OF THE APHID   109
    7. THE LIFE OF THE CHINCH BUG   121
    8. THE LIFE OF THE LACEWING FLY   131
    9. THE LIFE OF THE MONARCH BUTTERFLY   139
    10. THE LIFE OF THE HOUSEFLY   152
    11. THE LIFE OF THE LADYBIRD BEETLE   162
    12. THE LIFE OF THE CICADA-KILLER WASP   170
    13. THE LIFE OF THE PAPER-MAKING WASP   179
    14. THE LIFE OF THE ANT   186

BIBLIOGRAPHY   197

INDEX   203

ILLUSTRATIONS

Larva of the spicebush swallowtail	*facing page*	18
Hatching praying mantises	*following page*	18
Polistes wasp larva	*following page*	18
Eggs of the alderfly	" "	18
Nymphs of the alderfly	" "	18
Closeup of a dragonfly	" "	18
The tiger moth	" "	18
Head of a robber fly	" "	18
Face of a white-faced hornet	" "	18
The oval-winged katydid	*facing page*	19
The adult May fly	" "	82
A walking stick feeding	*following page*	82
A clinging dragonfly	" "	82
Termites exchanging food	*facing page*	83
A male black field cricket	" "	83
Two female crickets	" "	83
A praying mantis with a swallowtail	" "	114
A winged aphid	*following page*	114
The golden-eyed lacewing fly	" "	114
Head of a housefly	*facing page*	115
A monarch butterfly on a mallow	" "	178
The larva of the ladybird beetle	*following page*	178
A ladybird beetle feeding on aphides	" "	178
Galleries of the carpenter ant	" "	178
A cicada-killer wasp with its prey	*facing page*	179
The nest of the *Polistes* wasp	" "	179

PART I

THE STRANGENESS OF INSECT LIFE

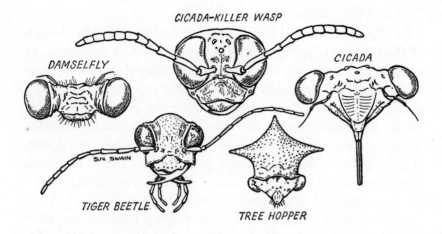

CICADA-KILLER WASP

DAMSELFLY

CICADA

S.N. SWAIN

TIGER BEETLE

TREE HOPPER

NINETEEN centuries ago, when Pliny the Elder was writing his natural history in Rome, men believed that insects were creatures without blood, that butterfly eggs were drops of solidified dew, that echoes killed honeybees, and that gold was mined in the mountains north of India by a giant ant "the color of a cat and as large as an Egyptian wolf."

"This gold," Pliny assured his readers, "is extracted in the winter and is taken by the Indians during the heats of summer while the ants are compelled by the excessive warmth to hide themselves in their holes. Still, however, on being aroused by catching the scent of the Indians, they sally forth and frequently tear them to pieces, though provided with the swiftest camels for the purpose of flight, so great is their fleetness, combined with their ferocity and their passion for gold."

Today, nobody credits Pliny's story of wolf-size ants with a passion for gold any more than they believe in his Oriental locusts that grew to such size that their hind legs were dried and used for saws. These traveler's tales, the product of imagination or misunderstanding, have been long discredited. Imaginary wonders, in fact, are less needed in dealing with the insects than with any other group of living creatures. The truth is odd and dramatic enough.

3

In 1857, when Alfred Russel Wallace landed on the Kei Islands of the Malay Archipelago to collect natural-history specimens, he soon noticed that each time he entered a deep damp forest glade he found the air filled with a fragrance that reminded him of attar of roses. For a long time he tried to trace the perfume to flowers. Finally he discovered that its source was not a flower but a beetle, the green and purple and yellow tiger beetle, *Therates labiatus*. It inhabited the damp and gloomy glades and fed mainly on insects that visited the flowers. Its perfume, Wallace concluded, aided it in attracting small nectar gatherers to the spot.

At least three species of Oriental praying mantises use color instead of perfume to aid them in securing their food. These insects, like the mantis native to the southern part of the United States, imprison their prey within the spined traps formed by their forelegs. By having parts of their bodies expanded into thin plates which are brightly tinted on the under side, the Oriental insects resemble flowers on the bushes where they hunt. When climbing to a favorable position, the mantis keeps the bright-colored under sides of the plates hidden. However, when it finds itself among flowers to its liking, it turns the colored surfaces uppermost and remains motionless until a victim alights close by.

One British naturalist reports seeing a mantis in India climb laboriously to the tips of three branches before it found flowers in bloom. On the first two times, when it found buds, it slowly retraced its steps and began again. Attaining the flowers, it took its position among them and exposed the under side of its pink, petal-like plates. Some Oriental mantises have plates that are blue, some mauve, some purple. Still others have pure white plates with a surface that is glistening and waxy, like the petals of real flowers.

In a number of instances, the *Orthoptera* of the tropics are ingeniously camouflaged by nature to escape the notice of their enemies. For example, the long-horned grasshopper, *Metaprosagoga insignis*, possesses wings which not only resemble leaves but which are equipped with irregular patches that look as though the leaf

4

tissue had been eaten away by an insect, leaving only a network of veins visible. Another tropical leaf-grasshopper has brownish wings that suggest dried leaves. The resemblance is heightened by the fact that markings near their extremities give the impression that they are cracked or torn. Then there is a mantis of the Orient, *Brancsikia aeroplana*, which has curled-up brownish edges to its wings, thus heightening their resemblance to dry brown leaves. On the wings of a katydid from Venezuela, which William Beebe once showed me, imitation dewdrops and fungus spots increased the effectiveness of the insect's camouflage.

Probably the most famous camouflaged insect in the world is *Kallima*, the dead-leaf butterfly of the Far East. In *The Malay Archipelago*, Alfred Russel Wallace tells of his first meeting with this remarkable butterfly. At the time he encountered it he was collecting in Sumatra, beating the bushes for insects and examining his net carefully for poisonous snakes, which were often dislodged from the branches, before extracting the insects he had caught.

"When on the wing," he writes of the dead-leaf butterfly, "it is very conspicuous. The species is not uncommon in dry woods and thickets and I often endeavored to catch it without success, for, after flying a short distance, it would enter a bush among dry or dead leaves and however carefully I crept up to the spot where the butterfly settled and though I lost sight of it for some time, I at length discovered that it was close before my eyes but that in its position of repose it so closely resembled a dead leaf attached to a twig as almost certainly to deceive the eye even when gazing full upon it.

"A very closely allied species, *Kallima inachis*, inhabits India where it is very common. No two are alike but all the variations correspond to those of dead leaves. Every tint of yellow, ash, brown, and red is found here and in many specimens there occur patches and spots formed of small black dots, so closely resembling the way in which minute fungi grow on leaves that it is almost impossible at first not to believe that fungi have grown on the butterflies themselves!"

5

Walking stick insects, in the tropics, also present some amazingly realistic instances of insect camouflage. One of the most remarkable bears the scientific name of *Achrioptera spinosissima*. About half a foot in length, its green and brown body is decorated with spines that are tinted bright red like thorns. The insect looks for all the world like a broken piece of briar moving along on six legs. Another tropical walking stick, *Palophus reyi*, is almost a foot long. The outer skin of its body is roughened into an amazingly close approximation of dry bark on a dead twig.

Such resemblances benefit the insect by making it inconspicuous amid its surroundings. But what benefit those brownie bugs of the insect world, the *Membracidae*, obtain from the fantastic adornments they possess is often difficult to see. Again, it is in the tropics that the most spectacular examples are found. Nature seems to have run riot, designing oddities just for the sake of originality. In some species of treehoppers, the prothorax is drawn out into hornlike adornments; in others, it rises in a high, curving crown; in others, it forms spears or balls. Oftentimes these are brightly colored. While American treehoppers are less extravagantly formed than those in the tropics, some species are among our oddest-appearing insects. All are small, and the strangeness of their forms frequently is unappreciated without the aid of a magnifying glass.

When Charles Darwin was crossing the Atlantic in 1832, at the start of his famous voyage in the *Beagle*, the ship dropped anchor at desolate St. Paul's Island, 540 miles from the coast of South America. "Not a single plant," Darwin writes, "not even a lichen, grows on this islet; yet it is inhabited by several insects and spiders." Most of them were parasites on the boobies and other sea birds that landed on the barren rocks and one was a small brown moth belonging to a genus that feeds on feathers.

The bleak cluster of volcanic rocks that forms St. Paul's Island is but one of many strange places where insects are able to survive.

Two insects that spend their early days under curious conditions are familiar to most parts of the United States. They are the rat-tailed maggot and the froghopper, the immature form of the Cercopidae. The former inhabits stagnant water or other waste fluids. It feeds on the bottom and breathes air through an extensible tube that forms its tail.

By surrounding itself with bubbles, the little froghopper produces its own climate. In spring and summer, small masses of froth often appear on grass stems and weeds. They are the foam castles of the cercopids. A kind of bicycle pump, formed of overlapping plates beneath its abdomen, which provide a chamber into which air is drawn and expelled, permits the insect to produce bubbles in excess sap which it has sucked from the plant. Within this bubble mass, sheltered from the direct rays of the sun and kept moist by the foam, the immature insect spends its early days. For millions of years, it has been employing its own primitive form of air conditioning.

One of the classic studies of the French entomologist, J. Henri Fabre, concerned the aerial journey of the wingless larva of the oil-beetle. Hatching from eggs deposited by the female insect close to flowering plants, the minute larvae slowly ascend the stems and lurk among the petals until a wild bee alights in search of pollen or nectar. Quickly the young beetle attaches itself to the hair on the bee's back and goes sailing through the air as a passenger when the winged insect flies back to its nest. Here the larva lets go. It has found its proper home, a place where it will be supplied with ample food until it transforms into an adult beetle. Not all larvae attach themselves to the right insects, but enough do to carry on the species by means of this ingenious stratagem.

Another instinctive stratagem is employed by an ant queen found in Tunis. She alights, after the nuptial flight in which she is fertilized by a male of her own species, near the nest of a larger species of ant. Workers seize her and drag her into the underground chambers. There she takes refuge on the back of the queen and remains unmolested. Using her opportunity, she eventually decapitates the rightful queen and is accepted as the new queen by

7

the workers. Her eggs develop workers of her own species and, in the end, the colony is made up of the smaller ants.

William Morton Wheeler, in his *Ants, Their Structure, Development and Behavior*, tells of a carnivorous butterfly larva that lives in the nests of an Australian ant where it feeds upon the young. An especially tough outer shell protects it from attacks by adult ants. In Queensland this remarkable butterfly, *Liphyra brassolis*, was studied by F. P. Dodd in the early years of the present century. The adult butterfly, emerging in the nest, is covered by fugitive scales, which save its life because the loose scales come off in the mandibles of the ants. In describing his observations, Dodd writes:

"Directly the ants encounter the scales they are in trouble. They fasten on to their feet and impede their movements, or, if their antennae or mandibles come in contact with any part of the butterfly, the scales adhere thereto, so that the ant is soon in a bad way and has quite enough to do in attempting to free herself of her incumbrances without taking any further interest in the butterfly. It is exceedingly ludicrous to observe the ants endeavoring to free themselves, their legs move awkwardly and their mandibles open and close in evident annoyance and perplexity, and they are also much concerned about the state of their antennae, for the obnoxious scales will not be shaken off, and they seem to become very low-spirited."

A number of insect oddities reveal their peculiar characteristics in defending themselves against attack. The blister beetle of southern Europe is equipped with a caustic fluid that protects it from its enemies. In olden times, such insects were ground up to form blistering ointments and plasters. A number of common insects, such as the familiar lady beetle, have weak places at the joints of their legs, which rupture to let out drops of disagreeable fluid when they are attacked.

As the polecat, among animals, relies on an offensive smell to repel its enemies, so a number of insects protect themselves by exuding disagreeable odors. Stink bugs are familiar to everyone. The lacewing, a pale-green, filmy little insect with golden eyes that lays stalked eggs from which hatch the aphis-lions that devour hordes of plant lice, is another skunk of the insect world. Handle one and the disagreeable fluid it exudes clings to your hands for hours.

Incidentally, the plant lice that are preyed upon by the immature lacewings are reported to employ a surprising method of defense occasionally when they are approached by the sickle-shaped, sucking jaws of an aphis-lion. The plump aphides produce, in addition to honeydew, a waxy secretion that collects at the ends of two tubes projecting backward from their abdomens. Before its enemy can use its jaws, an aphid sometimes will back quickly toward it, pushing the waxy blobs into its face. This sticky material halts the attack while the aphis-lion stops to clean away the wax.

The bluish-backed bombardier beetle, *Brachinus fumans*, gains time by a different ruse. When it is pursued by an enemy, it emits a little cloud of offensive gas. This gas attack takes the pursuer by surprise. It stops and the momentary pause is often sufficient to permit the beetle to escape.

These are active forms of defense. Other insects employ passive forms. They feign death to escape death. Otto Plath, in his *Bumblebees and Their Ways*, records an instance in which a robber fly was fighting with a bumble bee in a glass jar. Getting the worst of the battle, the fly suddenly fell on its back as though stung to death. It lay there, apparently lifeless, until Plath shook both insects out of the jar. Then the "dead" robber fly sprang into the air and darted away. Ambush bugs, lady beetles, monarch butterflies, and a long list of other insect opossums feign death. Some walking sticks will become rigid and apparently lifeless when alarmed. In one instance, a walking stick feigned death for six hours, remaining as rigid as a twig all during that time.

Giants and dwarfs among the insects cover a wide range. The great atlas moth of India, with a wingspread of a foot, and the Hercules beetle of Africa, which drones over the countryside at evening with a sound like an approaching airplane—those are

9

some of the giants. Among the pigmies are the microlepidoptera—tiny butterflies and moths—and fairy flies, which are built on such a miniature scale that, although they are perfect in all their parts, they measure only one-hundredth of an inch from head to tail.

In addition to oddities of size among the insects, there are innumerable oddities of form. Near the pyramids in Egypt early entomologists discovered a singular ant-lion with a slender and elongated neck. Its caliper jaws seem held at the end of an outstretched arm. This pipestem neck, in many instances, is far longer than the rest of the insect's body. It has been suggested that this lengthy neck permits the insect to secure its prey in deep crevices. A folding, extensible lip, which reaches out like a straightened arm to grasp underwater victims, is a feature of the head of every dragonfly nymph. At the end of the lip are grasping hooks, by means of which the nymph pulls its captive back into its mouth.

Enormous forelegs, more than twice the length of the rest of its body, are the characteristic of a black wood beetle discovered by Alfred Russel Wallace in the Moluccas. This beetle, *Euchirus longimanus*, covers a space of 8 inches with all its legs extended. Another insect curiosity of the Malay Archipelago is an antlered fly. Various species have protuberances on their heads that suggest the horns of deer, elk, and moose in miniature.

Even more remarkable is a stalk-eyed fly of South Africa, *Diopsis apicalis*. Like the hammerhead shark, it has its eyes extending out from the sides of its head. The stalks to which they are attached, however, are drawn out to such surprising length that the measurement from eye to eye is one-third more than the length of the body from head to tail.

An abdomen that has amazing powers of distention is a characteristic of the nymph of the bloodsucking *Rhodnius*. In a few minutes, one of these nymphs can distend itself with blood up to twelve times its original weight. As the huge meal is digested, the abdomen contracts smoothly like a deflating balloon. Similarly, the abdomens of the honey ants of the Southwest possess the ability

10

to expand enormously. Certain members of the colony act as storage vessels for the honeydew gathered by the workers. They never leave the nest. With abdomens so swollen they cannot walk, they cling to the roof of their underground chamber, regurgitating food to the workers when it is needed.

Various other ants must be numbered among the insect oddities. In *Ant-Hill Odyssey*, William M. Mann tells of collecting a species that is known to Brazilian natives as "The Terrible Ant." Fully an inch in length, it is said to produce a serious fever by its sting. A hundred years ago, when Henry W. Bates was collecting in the Amazon basin, he encountered villages that had been deserted because of an invasion of fire ants. These small red insects have stings like red-hot needles. Then there are the army ants that march in long lines in the jungle, the slave-making ants that raid other colonies for pupae, the tree ant of India, *Oecophylla smaragdina*, that uses its larvae as a means of sewing leaves together into a nest, passing the silk-producing grubs back and forth from one leaf edge to another to provide a solid bond. Within these leaf sheds, the ants keep smaller insects that produce honeydew, the sweet fluid upon which the ants feed.

Other insects have a taste for varied and often surprising things. That goat of the insect world, the drugstore beetle, is known to consume forty-five different substances, including the poisons aconite and belladonna. Other beetles feed on cigarettes, mustard plasters, and red pepper. Ants have shown themselves resistant to cyanide. Termites are able to digest cellulose in wood because of the aid of minute organisms within their intestines. In the case of some insects, a reduced diet slows down growth. Some wood-boring grubs, such as those of the cerambycid beetles, sometimes live in house timbers or furniture for years after they had been put in place. In one instance, an adult beetle emerged from a porch post that had been standing for twenty years. The dried timber lacks the nutritive qualities of the living tree and the growth of the grub is arrested, so long periods pass before it reaches maturity. Underground, the nymph of the periodical cicada spends more than a

11

decade and a half tunneling through darkness in the soil before it emerges into its brief life as an adult.

In the mating and reproduction activities of the insects, we find some of the strangest habits of all. The deathwatch beetle, that stand-by of ghost stories laid in old castles, bumps its head on the top of its wooden tunnel to send a kind of telegraphic message to its mate. To attract the attention of the females at mating time, the males of certain flies blow shining little bubbles of froth.

L. C. Miall, in *The Natural History of Aquatic Insects*, tells of a minute fly found in England under the bark of poplar, willow, and beech trees. It produces viviparously small larvae "which escape by tearing open the body of their parent and in turn produce other larvae after the same fashion."

These seem fantastic creatures and bizarre habits. But to one who views with fresh eyes the old, taken-for-granted, commonplace habits of even the most familiar insects—the everyday butterflies and grasshoppers and ants we see about us—there is in the events of their lives much that is a source of astonishment and wonder. A century ago, this amazing strangeness of the familiar insects was eloquently expressed in describing the metamorphosis of a moth in the early pages of the pioneer book on entomology by William Kirby and William Spence.

"Were a naturalist to announce to the world," they write, "the discovery of an animal which first existed in the form of a serpent; which then penetrated into the earth, and weaving a shroud of pure silk of the finest texture, contracted itself within this covering into a body without external mouth or limbs, and resembling, more than anything else, an Egyptian mummy; and which, lastly after remaining in this state without food and without motion . . . should at the end of that period burst its silken cerements, struggle through its earthly covering and start into day a winged bird—what think you would be the sensation excited by this strange piece of intelligence? After the first doubts of its truth were dispelled, what astonishment would succeed! Amongst the learned, what surmises!

12

—what investigations! Even the most torpid would flock to the sight of such a prodigy."

Almost everywhere in the world this strangeness of insect life is apparent. It is not confined to the jungles of the Malay Archipelago or to the forests of Equatorial Africa. It can be found in any backyard. You can observe it among the most common of the familiar insects. In the forms and organs and abilities of these tiny creatures, in the keenness of their senses, in the capacities that enable them to endure in spite of their insignificant size, you find a whole fresh realm of interest.

The second part of this book will deal with the world as the insect knows it. How does an insect see and feel and smell and find its way? How does it breathe and how does it discover its food? How is it born and how does it grow up and how does it die? What is the world like when seen from its viewpoint? What is it like to be an insect?

PART II

WHAT LIFE IS LIKE
FOR AN INSECT

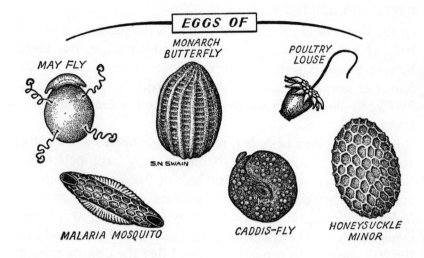

EGGS OF

MAY FLY

MONARCH
BUTTERFLY

POULTRY
LOUSE

S.N.SWAIN

MALARIA MOSQUITO

CADDIS-FLY

HONEYSUCKLE
MINOR

NEAR THE village of Elmo, in central Kansas, Dr. Frank M. Carpenter, a scientist from Harvard's Museum of Comparative Zoology, in 1935 unearthed the fossil remains of a prehistoric dragonfly. It was the world's largest, and one of its oldest, insects. On wings with a span of almost two and a half feet, this ancient dragonfly had hawked about over the great marshes and shallow seas of the Lower Permian Period, 200,000,000 years ago. Its many-faceted eyes saw a world so primitive that 20,000,000 years would pass before the coming of the dinosaurs.

In the Smithsonian Institution at Washington, D.C., there is a fossilized wasp nest which was discovered in southwestern Utah by two scientists of the U.S. Geological Survey, Dr. J. S. Reeside, Jr., and Dr. C. E. Dobbin. It was constructed 80,000,000 years ago. The wasps which chewed wood fibers into the pulp-paper of which the nest is made were among the world's first pollen carriers. They helped fertilize the pioneer blooms of the late Cretaceous.

Many parts of the world have contributed other fossils of ancient insects. In spite of their relative smallness and frailness, insects of a long-ago past have been preserved in coal, in limestone, in amber. I have, in a drawer of my desk, a piece of transparent amber about twice the size of a postage stamp. It was picked up

17

on the shores of the Baltic Sea. Within is the perfectly preserved body of a flylike insect. Some 50,000,000 years ago, this insect became entangled in pitch oozing from a tree in the great coniferous forests of northern Europe. The pitch had turned to amber, or fossilized resin, and the insect—a fossil within a fossil—remained intact within.

From such pieces of amber, scientists have obtained more than 1000 different kinds of insects. Nearly as many fossil species have been recovered from the Miocene beds of Bavaria. And well over 1000 more have come from the Florissant deposits of Colorado. Volcanic ash, drifting down after eruptions of long ago, buried many insects near Florissant in a fine drift that solidified and held the frail creatures so perfectly preserved that the delicate veins of their wings can be studied by scientists millions of years later.

A total of about 12,000 species of fossil insects have been described by entomologists. They have come from England, Scotland, France, Russia, Sweden, Switzerland, the United States, Australia, New Brunswick, Canada, New South Wales, and other countries. Four-fifths of them belong to orders and families which exist today. The story of these fossils is a record of the antiquity of the insects and of their world-wide distribution in prehistoric times.

For nearly 200,000,000 years before man appeared on the planet, the insects had been a feature of its fauna. How they originated is not definitely known. It seems most probable that they descended from some crablike ancestor which crept up out of the steaming shallow seas to become an air-breathing inhabitant of the land. The modern insect differs from all other living creatures in having, in its adult form, six legs and a jointed body. Spiders and daddy-longlegs and millipedes and sow bugs are not insects. They have too many legs. In popular usage, many of these small creatures are lumped in with the insects. In 1940, when the U.S. Government Printing Office issued a list of pamphlets available on insects, a bulletin on earthworms was included in the catalogue; and, two centuries ago, when a description of the insects of North America was published by a pioneer naturalist, snakes were listed among

18

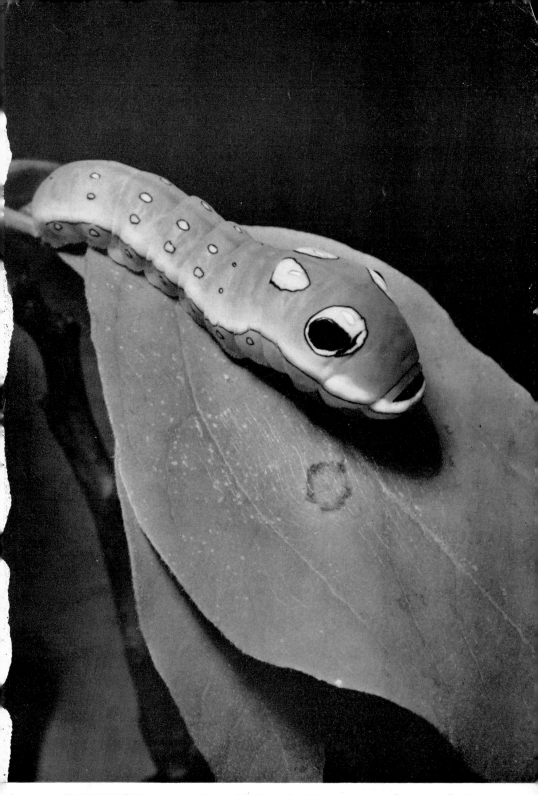

IMITATION eyes, two large black and yellow spots on the green body of a spicebush swallowtail larva, create the illusion of the head of a snake.

EARLY DAYS of insects. Top left, praying mantises hatching; right, a larva of the *Polistes* wasp. Below, eggs and hatching nymphs of the alderfly.

THE DRAGONFLY and tiger moth (top), robber fly and white-faced hornet (below), illustrate how legs, antennae, eyes, and jaws are adapted for special tasks.

THE KATYDID, a relative of the grasshopper, rasps its green, leaflike wings together to produce the call that repeats its name.

the insects.

The silverfish, that pale, streamlined, wingless creature sometimes found under piles of papers in the basement or among long-stored books, is the oldest living insect. The cockroach and the dragonfly are other hexapods of ancient lineage. These three are, according to the length of their family line, the aristocrats of the insect world. The ants, with their communal labors and complex social system, are a development of a considerably later period.

Present-day insects, the descendants of these fossil pioneers, have spread to every habitable area on the face of the globe. Virtually everywhere man has gone, he has found the insects there before him. Seven hundred miles north of the Arctic Circle, survivors from the ill-fated *Jeannette* were amazed to see a butterfly. Thirty-five thousand feet above sea level, a balloonist noticed a honeybee flying around the wicker basket of his craft. Hundreds of miles from the nearest coastline, mariners have seen water-striders skating over the surface of the swells. These marine insects lay their eggs on floating sea-bird feathers and other bits of refuse and often spend their whole lives out of sight of land.

High in the Himalayas, and in the Alps, mountain climbers have found insects in action. A praying mantis was discovered 16,000 feet above sea level. In Ecuador, butterflies were sighted among the crags of the Andes at 16,500 feet. The moth *Erebus*, in South America, is encountered all the way from lowland swamps up to 10,000 feet on mountainsides. When airplanes carrying U.S. Department of Agriculture scientists combed the air above 300,000 acres of Louisiana forest and swampland, some years ago, they caught redlegged grasshoppers at 1000 feet. Plates, coated with a thin layer of castor oil and resin, trapped the insects encountered. Even creatures like wingless plant lice are carried far into the sky by strong up-currents. At a height of 200 feet, the scientists calculated, there is an insect for every 6748 cubic feet of air. One mile above the earth the ratio is one insect for each 117,546 cubic feet.

Some insects dwell in the mud of hot springs where the water is

19

almost boiling. Others inhabit cold mountain crevices where the temperature remains near the freezing point. The "ice bug" or "alpine rock crawler" is one of these. Found only at high elevations of from 5400 to 8600 feet, it is active when most other insects are paralyzed by cold. It suffers heat prostration if the mercury reaches eighty degrees F. This primitive insect has the scientific name of *Grylloblatta campodeiformis*, which, translated roughly, means "the cricket-cockroach shaped like a caterpillar." Tiny springtails, or "snow fleas," sometimes appear by the million on the surface of midwinter drifts. In pools of petroleum, insects—breathing through tubes thrust above the surface of the oil—make their home; in the Great Salt Lake, where the water is more salty than it is in the sea, other insects dwell. Underground, in the great caverns of the earth, there are colorless and virtually blind insect inhabitants, cave-dwellers that never see daylight.

Wherever there is sufficient moisture, warmth, and food to support life, there the insects are well established. These three requirements are found most abundantly in the tropics. There, insect life reaches its peak. In 1870 the entomologist James Orton pointed out that in Greenland there are only eleven species of insects; in England, 2500; and in Brazil, 8000. While the number of species known to science has increased vastly since his time, the point of his comparison still holds good. The insect population reaches its maximum in the tropics and decreases as the traveler moves away toward either pole. Both in number of species and in number of individuals, the insects exceed any other visible form of life on earth.

At the present time, the number of species of insects which have been described and named by scientists stands at more than 685,000. It is pretty well agreed that there must be several million kinds of these six-legged creatures inhabiting the earth. They range from microscopic beetles able, literally, to creep through the eye of a needle, to a giant walking stick from the island of New Guinea fifteen inches long.

20

Judged by the number of species, this is the Age of the Beetles. Almost one out of every three species of insects catalogued by science is a beetle. The grand total of their varying forms is about 277,000 for the entire world and more than 26,600 for North America north of Mexico. The butterflies and moths come next with approximately 112,000 species. The *Hymenoptera*, including the wasps, ants, and bees, have slightly more than 100,000, while the flies number about 85,000 species. When Alfred Russel Wallace returned to England from his celebrated travels in the Malay Archipelago eighty years ago, he brought among other things 280 different kinds of ants. Two hundred of them proved to be species unknown to science. Those virgin days, when almost everything brought back from a trip of exploration was an addition to zoological knowledge, have passed. Still, new species of insects are being added to the lists each month; as many as 6000 have been described in the course of a single recent year.

The plants of the world which have been described by botanists number only about 250,000 species. The different kinds of animals, other than insects, known to science are even fewer—215,000. Of the 900,000 forms of animal life in the world, at least 685,000 are insects. Furthermore, each insect usually appears in several forms, such as the egg, larva or nymph, pupa, and adult. This fact multiplies infinitely the number of differently formed insects it is possible to encounter. Also, each species of insect is represented by a vast number of individuals. Of all living creatures on the face of the earth, fully nine-tenths are insects.

It is thus not surprising that the world of the insects is still largely unexplored. Even among the common insects, so much remains to be learned that scientists know the complete life-story of hardly 10 per cent of the species. If entomological textbooks included blank pages to indicate the unknown, there would be hundreds of such pages for every one on which printing appeared.

Measuring the length of the insect world in time, we see it extends for 200,000,000 years and more into the past; measuring its width in the number of different species, we find its spread is farther than that of any other form of animal life; measuring its depth in the number of individuals, we learn that it comprises more than ninety per cent of living forms. The insects are, as they have been since prehistoric times, the most widespread and successful form of animal life.

Many species have descended through the ages virtually unchanged. Ants found in Baltic amber are often structurally no different from those alive today. The beetle still "wheels his droning flight" over the English countryside just as it did in the time of Thomas Gray; the bee Napoleon Bonaparte chose for his crest still makes honey among the flower-filled fields of France; the scarab beetle of the Nile follows the pattern of its life just as it did when the land was under the rule of the Pharaohs; mosquitoes rise from the marshes of southern Europe as they rose to greet the soldiers of Caesar; and crickets chirp in China just as they sang in the courts of the rulers in 1000 B.C.

During their long history, the insects have survived because they have adapted themselves to a succession of constantly altering conditions. They have met innumerable changes and have ridden out countless storms. They have endured where other forms of life succumbed. This has been due to several factors.

The first is the smallness of the insects. It takes no great amount of food or water to sustain the individual. Insects can survive on starvation rations and can live in places where larger animals would die. The second factor is the number of individuals. The fate of the species never rests on a few. If a thousand and one fail and perish, the thousand-and-second may succeed, live, and carry on the species. Still another point of importance is the shortness of the life cycle of most insects. They may have several generations in a single summer. Thus, evolution is speeded up and it is easier for insects to alter their forms and characteristics to meet new conditions than it is for longer-lived and larger animals.

In the curious life habits and the often mystifying abilities of the insects there are still other factors which have aided their spread and survival. Anyone who contemplates their ways closely must feel that there is justification for Maurice Maeterlinck's conclusion: "The insect does not belong to our world. The other animals, the plants even, notwithstanding their dumb life and the secrets which they cherish, do not seem wholly foreign to us. In spite of all, we feel a certain earthly brotherhood in them. They often surprise and amaze our intelligence, but do not utterly upset it. There is something, on the other hand, about the insect that does not seem to belong to the habits, the ethics, the psychology of our globe."

An insect breathes but it has no lungs. It hears but it has no ears on its head. It smells but it has no nose. Its heart pumps blood but it is so unlike our hearts that it often reverses itself and beats backward. Even the way an insect sees and walks and flies is individual to itself. From birth to death, it is a creature of strange habits and puzzling abilities, a creature surrounded by many mysteries.

AN INSECT IS BORN in one of several ways. Grasshoppers hatch from eggs laid in the ground or amid plant tissues the previous autumn. The newborn are minute and wingless, but they are undeniably grasshoppers. Midsummer aphides are born alive. They are produced by parthenogenesis, or virgin birth, by mothers that were themselves produced in the same way. They, like the grasshoppers, are miniature models of the older insects. But in many other species, the young insects appear in forms not even remotely resembling the adults.

A baby monarch butterfly creeps from the egg as a caterpillar. A dragonfly is born underwater as a nymph. It breathes by means of gills and lives the life of a fish. The young of the paper-making wasp come from the eggs within the six-sided cells as footless and helpless grubs, fed and cared for by the nurses of the colony. The immature housefly is a maggot; the young of the May beetle is a "grubworm"; the child of the lacewing fly is a dark, lizard-like

23

midget, a hunter of plant lice. Except among the social species, few insect mothers ever see their offspring. The young are equipped by instinct to take care of themselves.

In northern states, most insects appear in spring from eggs laid by the females the previous autumn. These eggs may be deposited in water, in plant tissues, beneath the bark of a dead tree, in the soil, cemented to rocks, put in any one of a host of hiding places. Different eggs require different situations. Mosquito eggs, for example, will hatch well only in stagnant water. They seem to require chemicals given off by decaying vegetation. Many insect eggs are sculptured and tinted microscopic gems, particularly those of the *Hemiptera*, or true bugs. Oftentimes they are decorated with elaborate patterns, circles of spikes, gold plating, and bands of crimson and green. Seen under a microscope, they are things of beauty and color. The eggs of the wheelbug are shaped like elongated jugs while those of one of the aquatic insects have the exact appearance of old-fashioned beer barrels, even to the hoops and bung.

The average number of eggs deposited during the life of a female insect is estimated at approximately 100. Some produce far more than this. A dobson fly will lay as many as 3000 eggs in a compact mass hardly more than half an inch across. A queen honeybee sometimes lays that many eggs in a single day. The termite queens of the tropics are the champion egg-producers among the insects. One of these creatures during her lifetime may produce tens of millions of eggs. A curious feature of some insect eggs is their ability to multiply and to produce more than one individual. From a single egg of a parasitic chalcid fly, laid in the body of a victim, upwards of 2000 young insects will develop. The original egg keeps multiplying, almost in the manner of an amoeba.

According to their kind, insects have two, three, or four different stages in their development. The bees, wasps, beetles, butterflies, moths, flies, and some other insects have what is called a complete metamorphosis. They appear in four different forms during their lifetime: first the egg, then the larva, then the pupa, and finally the adult. Other species, which skip one or more of these stages, are said to have an incomplete metamorphosis. Grasshoppers, crickets, chinch bugs, and others appear as eggs and as young insects that resemble the adults sufficiently to be recognized. They reach adulthood through a series of changes or molts. Dragonflies and cicadas are representatives of the three-stage development in which there is first the egg, then the nymph, and third the adult.

In some rare cases, the larva or even the pupa may give birth to living young. This has been observed among the *Cecidomyiidae*, a group of flies which include the destructive Hessian fly and the wheat midge. The young of the genus *Miastor* sometimes produce eggs before they are out of the larval or pupal stage. These eggs hatch within their bodies and the ravenous larvae which emerge immediately begin devouring their parents. To prevent a like fate, some of the ichneumon flies, those wasplike parasites which deposit their eggs in the body tissues of caterpillars, have to scatter their eggs while in flight at times when they are unable to find their prey and the eggs are ready to hatch within their bodies.

In other instances, parasitic *Diptera* deposit their offspring as pupae rather than as larvae. Even stranger is the habit of the human botfly. It seeks out not humans but mosquitoes. On these insects it deposits its eggs—eggs that are highly susceptible to the body temperatures of human beings. When, later on, the mosquito alights on a human, the warmth induces a sudden hatching and the baby fly burrows into the skin. The adults of these flies, *Dermatobia hominis*, seize mosquitoes as they are emerging in a marshy place, deposit ten or a dozen eggs on their legs or abdomens, and then release them. From then on, they can depend upon the mosquitoes to find a home for the baby botflies.

Many of the reproductive habits of insects are so strange they are almost beyond belief. But the baby insect which is produced almost always has the same immediate goal in life: to eat and to grow as rapidly as it can.

25

AN INSECT GROWS in a series of sudden expansions known as molts. It is during its immature stages that the creature does all its growing. Once it becomes an adult, it grows no more. Its size is fixed. From then on, it eats to live rather than to grow. A small winged fly never becomes a big winged fly; a small-sized bumblebee always remains a small-sized bumblebee. When these insects have attained their wings, they are adults and their period of growth has ended.

It is during growing time that insect pests are most destructive. It is the caterpillar that does the harm and not the butterfly; it is the larva of the clothes moth that eats holes in dresses and coats and not the winged adult. The appetite of a growing insect probably exceeds that of any other living creature. A ravenous beetle larva will consume its own weight in food in twenty-four hours. During its last day as a larva, the immature honeybee is fed as many as 1200 meals by the workers. In fifty-six days, one research scientist calculated, the caterpillar of the American silk moth, *Telea polyphemus*, will devour so much leaf tissue that its weight will increase as much as 4140 times.

When a chick or a kitten or a human baby grows, its skin grows with it, keeping pace with its increase in size. But the skin of an insect cannot do this. It is hard and stiff like a suit of armor. Besides being its skin, the insect's shell is also its skeleton. An insect has no internal framework of bones. Its muscles are attached to the inside of its shell. Because it can grow no larger than the suit of armor which encloses it, the insect has to shed its outer shell at intervals. This change is called a molt; the period between molts is called an instar.

The remarkable material which makes up the outer shell of an insect's body is insoluble in water and resistant to alcohol, concentrated alkalis, and diluted acids. It is known as chitin and has a complex chemical composition which is identical with that of fungine, a plant-world material found in the cell walls of fungi. In innumerable forms, chitin appears in the bodies of the insects. It forms the horny armor of the beetles as well as the thin skins of

26

the caterpillars. Some transparent internal plates of chitin have been revealed by the electronic microscope to be only a quarter of a millionth of an inch in thickness.

As the immature insect develops, its suit becomes too small. Liquid known as molting fluid forms between the old skin and the soft, folded new skin beneath. This fluid acts as a lubricant when the insect sheds its hard, outgrown suit of armor. It also digests part of the inner surface of the old skin in preparation for the molting. By swallowing quantities of air or water, some insects increase the pressure within their bodies in order to split the old chitin shell. Others force the body fluids forward into the thorax, or mid-body, until the outer skin splits along the back.

The soft, rumpled body of the insect appears through this rent. The creature pulls forth its antennae, its legs, its abdomen. Sometimes it swallows a quantity of air again to "inflate" itself and increase its size in order to smooth out the folds of its new and larger skin. This gradually hardens into the shell which the insect will wear during its next instar. After each molt, as a general rule, the consumption of food increases. In many insects during the immature stages, a leg or antenna which is broken off will grow out again.

Once the chitin shell has hardened, it provides the creature it houses with a skeleton of exceptional strength. Insects, in proportion to their size, are the strongest animals on earth. By placing tiny bags of shot on the back of one scarabaeid beetle, a scientist found that the insect, although it weighed only 4⅕ grams, could support and carry a total weight of 8¼ ounces, or more than 850 times its own weight. A bumblebee, attached by a thread to a weighted miniature toy car, dragged a load more than 300 times its own weight. An elephant can barely drag twice its weight. Proportionately, then, a bee is 150 times as strong as an elephant!

The number of molts made by an insect varies according to its species. Some insects reach maturity with one or two molts; the May fly may have as many as twenty, and the seventeen-year cicada as many as thirty. A curious paradox in molting is the action of a

27

clothes-moth larva with insufficient food. It sometimes goes into a "molting frenzy," changing its skin repeatedly and getting smaller and smaller with each change.

For the grasshoppers, crickets, flies, and similar insects, the final molt produces the wings. They appear as wing-pads at the time of the next-to-final molt. For the *Lepidoptera* and the other insects that have a complete metamorphosis, the larva reaches its full size and then turns into a pupa. Butterflies produce naked pupa-cases or chrysalises. Moths frequently surround the pupa with a silken envelope or cocoon. The making of such a cocoon will often consume the better part of a day. One scientist watched a polyphemus caterpillar starting its cocoon and counted the movements it made. He estimated that it required more than 250,000 movements of the larva's head to complete the job. The silk comes from glands opening into the larva's mouth. Beetles come from naked pupa-cases. Sometimes they are buried in the ground or placed under bark and at other times they are attached to the underside of leaves. The length of the pupal stage has a wide range. But when it ends, the pupa-case splits and the adult insect emerges. Its period of growth is over and it has reached its final form.

AN INSECT EATS during the various stages of its life an infinite and surprising variety of foods. Cockroaches devour everything from wallpaper to water-color paints, from whitewash to honey, from bedbugs to stale beer. Some insects feed on pollen, some on decaying animals, some on wood. Leaf-miners tunnel through the tissues of the interior of leaves. Aphides thrust their sharp sucking-spears into plants and drink from a flowing well of sap. Dragonflies scoop insect prey from the air. Katydids and walking sticks nibble leaves.

Among the hosts of the beetles the greatest variety in diet is found. Some beetles hunt down living prey by the swiftness of their limbs; others spend their days consuming foliage; others bore through wood; others riddle stored cigarettes; and still others, as we have seen, dine on drugstore supplies that range from mustard plasters to bug poisons. So strong are the jaws of beetles that one has gained the nickname of "the short-circuit beetle" by tunneling into the lead of electric cables.

In a number of instances the immature and the adult insects desire far different fares. Baby wasps crave meat while the adults are mainly nourished on nectar. The larva of a butterfly has jaws for munching leaves whereas the adult possesses only a coiled sipping proboscis useful for obtaining nothing but liquid nourishment. Again, the male and the female insects of the same species may—like Jack Spratt and his wife—have entirely different tastes in the matter of food. The female mosquito, for example, dines on blood while the male is content with nectar. The mosquito that bites you is never a male. It always is a female.

AN INSECT OBTAINS ITS FOOD by plying many trades. Among insects there are hunters, trappers, farmers, fishermen, scavengers, miners. The underwater, immature caddis fly constructs, in brooks and streams, little nets among the pebbles in which it seines out the small organisms which form its food. Robber flies, riding on swift wings, swoop down like hawks upon smaller aerial insects and, wrapping their long, clawed legs about the bodies of their victims, carry them off to some perch where they dine at leisure. Dragonflies also hawk about, catching their food on the wing. Tiger beetles race over the hot sand of open stretches on slender, swift legs to pounce like cats upon their food.

Some ants carry vegetable matter into their underground nests to form a kind of compost on which a fungus will grow. From these fungus-gardens they reap a harvest of food. Other ants gather seeds and store them away in subterranean granaries. Honeybees fill the six-sided wax cells of their comb with honey to provide food for the winter. Coming from afar, guided by an amazingly delicate sense of smell, the carrion beetles assemble wherever there is a dead bird or mouse, even in the heart of a city.

Other insects obtain their food by stealth and artfulness. The green or brown praying mantis remains motionless among leaves, virtually hidden by its camouflage coloring, until a victim approaches within reach. The predaceous ambush bug is similarly hidden by its greens and browns and yellows. Only when it moves does it become apparent among the florets of a buddleia bloom. Ant-lions use strategy instead of speed or camouflage to catch their prey. Excavating a conical pit in loose sand, they bury themselves at the bottom with only their sickle-shaped jaws protruding. When an unwary ant blunders into the pit and begins sliding down the steep embankment, the buried insect sends up a sudden shower of quartz particles that hastens the landslide and brings the victim within reach of its terrible jaws.

This digger of pits is but one of many insects that use stratagems and ideas that man also employs. The sting of a wasp is a natural hypodermic needle; the water beetle's eye, divided in half with the upper part for seeing in air and the lower part for seeing in water, is the original model of bifocal glasses; the breathing tube of a rat-tailed maggot is the prototype of the diving gear; the spiked fore-legs of the praying mantis are nature's original patent-model for the toothed steel trap; the ovipositor of the ichneumon fly, *Megarhyssa lunator*, is an efficient drill; the sucking mechanism of a butterfly duplicates the idea which makes possible the fountain pen. The insects, as the writer of Proverbs observed of the ant and the locust, "are little upon the earth, but they are exceeding wise."

AN INSECT AVOIDS ITS ENEMIES by the employment of other stratagems and ruses. The monarch butterfly, ladybird beetle, ambush bug, robber fly, and other insects will feign death when in danger. Lacewing flies give off an evil-smelling fluid which repels their enemies. The bombardier beetle shoots out jets of gas which have the same effect.

The larva of the monarch, with its brilliantly marked black and yellow body, is protected by nauseating blood which makes birds sick and causes them to avoid the caterpillars. The larva of the spicebush swallowtail butterfly, *Papilio troilus*, has no such protection. Instead it has two great staring yellow and black eye-spots on the swollen forepart of its green body. Birds sometimes dart away screaming in terror when they come upon these harmless larvae among the leaves. The eye-spots give the caterpillar the appearance of the reared head of a green snake. In addition, this larva, as well as the caterpillars of the black swallowtail, can thrust out brilliant orange horns which give off an evil odor that repels would-be attackers.

Protective coloration saves the lives of many insects. Everyone has seen one of the underwing *Catocala* moths alight on a tree trunk, cover its brilliantly-colored hind wings with its drab fore wings, and apparently vanish. Some of the tiger beetles make a quick sidewise dart at the end of a run, thus making it more difficult to follow them with the eye. The familiar katydid, with its green, veined wings, is rarely observed unless it is in motion. It is an almost perfect imitation leaf.

One of the most puzzling aspects of insect protection is so-called mimicry. The best-known instance of the kind is that of the monarch and the viceroy butterflies. The monarch is avoided by birds because of its nauseating blood. The viceroy, a butterfly of an entirely different family, with different life habits and devoid of the monarch's evil-tasting blood, is so closely patterned after the monarch in its wing design that a second glance is needed to distinguish between the two. Birds apparently avoid the viceroy just as they do the monarch. Thus this butterfly, by looking like an insect that is immune to attacks, also enjoys immunity.

There are numerous other instances in which insects appear to benefit from their close resemblance to other and better-protected species. One Oriental ant mimics a wasp even to the extent of having markings that give it the appearance of having the thin thread-waist of the sting-bearing insect. A robber fly found in many parts of the United States is such a perfect imitation of a bumblebee that, unless the insects are at rest, it is almost impossible to tell them apart.

AN INSECT GETS ITS COLOR in one of two different ways. The hues are produced either by pigments or by minute ridges and grooves in the chitin of the outer shell, or scales, of the insect's

31

body. The pigment often is obtained from the food consumed. The green of many caterpillars is derived from the chlorophyll in the leaves which make up the creature's diet. Yellow and red pigment also may come from food. Dr. S. W. Frost, Professor of Economic Entomology at Pennsylvania State College, reports that an insect which preys upon the Colorado potato beetle obtains its yellow color pigment from the potato beetle which has, in turn, obtained it from the leaves of the potato plants it has consumed. The chalky white of the cabbage butterfly's wings is derived from uric acid.

After an insect's death, the colors produced by pigments often fade. Dragonflies are, in life, gorgeous creatures of shining, brilliant blues and greens and reds and varied hues. In death they usually soon become dull and lusterless. Some other insects, which do not depend upon pigments for their colors, remain as vivid after death as they are in life.

The celebrated morpho butterflies of the tropics, with their iridescent shimmering blue wings, are among these latter insects. Some beetles also possess especially brilliant metallic coloration. In reality such insects are colorless. Yet they have the most brilliant colors of all. This paradox lies in the formation of their scales or the exterior shells of their bodies.

Each one of the nearly 1,000,000 scales on the wings of a large morpho is covered with minute ridges and grooves. They are so tiny no human eye, unaided, can see them. There are as many as 1400 ridges in a single millimeter. These ridges and grooves act in the manner of a prism, breaking up the light. They are set at exactly the right angle to reflect to our eyes nothing but the blue rays. Similarly, the metallic greens of some tiger and wood-boring beetles are produced by grooves and ridges. So long as these grooves and ridges remain undamaged, the brilliant coloring of the insect persists.

AN INSECT SEES both color and movement through eyes that are far different from ours. Instead of one lens in each eye, an insect may have thousands of lenses. Instead of focusing on objects at different distances, as we do, the eye of an insect is like a fixed-focus camera lens. An insect sleeps with its eyes open; it has no way of closing them.

The number of lenses in the compound eye of an insect varies with the species and the kind of life the animal leads. Ants, moving slowly and close to the ground, depend largely on their sense of smell and have poor eyesight. Some ant eyes have no more than fifty lenses. A swift robber fly, which depends upon its eyesight to see and follow its aerial prey, has immense eyes, containing thousands of lenses and bulging outward from its head. Some dragonflies have as many as 30,000 lenses in a single eye. Each lens is six-sided. Fitting together, they form a great compound organ of sight covering most of the insect's head. It bulges outward so the dragonfly can see ahead, behind, above and below all at the same time. In the manner of a mosaic each lens contributes a part of the picture seen by the compound eye. Between the compound eyes of insects there are several simple eyes. They seem to be used for detecting differences between light and dark rather than for seeing.

While it is doubtful that insects can see objects sharply, as we can, some of them can see what our eyes cannot—the "black light" of the ultraviolet. Numerous tests, for example, have proved that honeybees can see by means of ultraviolet rays. How far an insect can see is a much-debated question. Many insects undoubtedly are near-sighted in the extreme. Others like the dragonfly and the flies which prey on the Western antelope can see for considerable distances. As an insect grows and develops through the different molts, it usually adds more lenses, or facets, to its eyes. As a general rule, the eyes are largest in the adult form.

AN INSECT SMELLS usually by means of its antennae. They form its nose. The antennae of the May beetle, for instance, contain something like 40,000 tiny olfactory pits. The great fern-like feelers of the Cecropia and Polyphemus moths provide these night-flying insects with smelling organs infinitely more sensitive than the nose of the most keen-scented bloodhound. After moths have

33

been marked and released, they have proved their ability to follow faint scent trails through the air for seven miles and more in order to reach the location of a virgin female. Ants follow a trail of formic acid laid down by the workers of a colony, thus finding their way home by means of their feelers. Cut off the antennae of the moth or ant and it is lost.

Through its sense of smell the great orange ichneumon fly, *Megarhyssa lunator*, locates the larvae of the sawfly, *Tremex*, which are tunneling through logs. Some ichneumon flies have such keen antennae that they can detect the presence of a victim through two solid inches of wood. In many cases, instinctive acts are set in motion by certain odors. Some flies feed on nectar but lay their eggs in putrid matter. The smell of nectar or honey induces them to eat; the smell of decaying garbage produces reactions that induce them to lay their eggs.

AN INSECT HEARS, if it does hear, through oddly placed organs for sound detection far different from the familiar ears of larger animals. The short-horned grasshopper, or locust, has its ears located on the sides of its abdomen. The katydid and the cricket carry their ears just below their "knees" on their front legs. Some butterflies have ears near the base of their wings on the thorax.

Fine hairs on the bodies of various caterpillars, such as those of the familiar mourning cloak butterfly, respond to sound vibrations and can be classed as hearing organs. The same is true of the cerci, those spike-like organs which project to the rear from the bodies of crickets and cockroaches. They are equipped with delicate hairs and they, too, respond to sound waves. The bottle-brush antennae of male gnats and mosquitoes quiver in response to the hum of the females. Hearing through their antennae, the males find the females in the dark.

Numerous insects show no sign that they possess a sense of hearing at all. Honeybees appear to live in a world devoid of sounds. They detect vibrations in the hive but, so far as can be determined, do not hear sound waves. Dragonflies and ants also seem to be entirely deaf. The insects which do hear catch insect-produced sounds which are made in various ways. The male cicada's shrill "bur-r-r-r" is created by taut membranes beneath the base of the insect's wings. The fiddling of the cricket, the meadow grasshopper and the katydid is accomplished by scraping one wing over the other. The crackle of the hovering locust comes from its hind wings rubbing on the forewings. In some instances sounds are of a double origin. The buzz of the gnat is a combination of a shrill note and a deeper note. The latter is the product of the rapidly moving wings while the former is due to the vibration of tense membranes at the openings of some of the insect's breathing tubes.

AN INSECT FEELS earth-borne vibrations and detects the nature of its surroundings through the aid of several bodily mechanisms. Tactile spines and hairs provide most insects with a sense of touch. We are able to tell the position of our limbs by the "feel" of the muscles. Many insects apparently cannot do this. They possess small hairs which are bent when the legs are folded. This enables the insect to know the position of its limbs.

Cave-dwelling crickets have special tactile hairs on their antennae which assist them in finding their way about the black interior of the caverns in which they live. A fringe of tiny hairs, and scales which are equipped with nerves, enable some species of butterflies to "feel" the position of their wings as they are folded on alighting. These hairs and scales along the margins of the wings may also respond to air movements during flight. Some scientists also suggest that the numerous hairs on antennae of night-flying insects may be sensitive to changes in air currents and thus may enable the insects to avoid hitting objects in the dark.

AN INSECT TASTES what it eats by means of both exterior and interior organs. Some of these are located within the mouth; others are situated in the palpi, those fingerlike organs found beside the mouths of many insects. By means of their palpi, the praying mantis, grasshopper, butterfly, and cricket tell what they are

35

eating. The palpi are the main organs of taste, but they are not the only ones.

That many species of insects have delicate senses of taste has been demonstrated innumerable times. By rewarding a *Dytiscus* diving beetle with bits of sweetened meat and punishing it with bits of quinine-treated meat, one scientist found he could teach the beetle to associate a certain taste with the presence of desired food. A beetle which was accustomed to being fed after a salty taste, for example, would go to salt-treated cotton batting and disregard sweetened cotton batting. Through its palpi, largely, it was able to distinguish between the taste qualities: sweet, bitter, salt. Tests on bark beetles and crickets revealed they could detect sweet tastes by means of their palpi.

Bees reject honey if it is given a bitter or salty taste. If small amounts of quinine are added, the bees refuse to touch it. Sensory pits at the base of the honeybee's tongue are believed to be its primary organs of taste. Various caterpillars will hastily spit out bits of leaves which have been treated with salt, bitter, or acid substances. The taste organs of these larvae are apparently within the mouth.

In addition to having sensory organs at the base of the tongue, honeybees appear able to taste with their antennae and with their feet. Butterflies and flies have similar taste organs on their feet. Fruit flies and houseflies can detect sweetened water as soon as their feet come in contact with it. A monarch butterfly or a red admiral will uncurl its proboscis when it steps into sweetened water but will give no response when the water is plain. The taste organs in the legs of these insects are located on the soles of their feet. A mourning cloak is also sensitive to sweetened water. Touch the tarsi of one of these insects with a paintbrush dipped in such fluid, and it immediately uncoils its proboscis.

What seems sweet to us, however, sometimes does not seem sweet to an insect. One laboratory worker tested thirty different substances which seem sweet to the human tongue, trying them out on honeybees. The insects responded to only nine. The sense of

36

taste among insects appears erratic and varies widely with different orders and species. When ants were tested on sweets, different species responded to different numbers; some species rejected a sweet that another species accepted. In some instances the taste sense of an insect is keener than that of a man. A honeybee, for example, can detect a concentration of salt that produces no effect at all on the human tongue.

AN INSECT BREATHES through an elaborate system of branching air-tubes. There are no lungs in the body of an insect. The air is drawn in through openings in the body-shell called spiracles. Such openings can be seen, running like a line of portholes along the side of a ship, on the abdomen of a locust or grasshopper. The tubes into which the air rushes are frequently braced by spiral bands of chitin. Larger tubes branch into smaller tubes and these in turn branch into still smaller tubes to form a network that carries oxygen directly to all parts of the body.

Diving beetles have fine hair, or pile, on the underside of their bodies. This coating of hair catches and holds air which the insect breathes during its long periods of submergence. The larva of one of the Syrphid flies, *Eristalis tenax*, has a breathing apparatus that suggests a diving suit. This larva feeds on decaying matter at the bottom of rain-filled knotholes and other small openings. From the end of its body a curious telescoping tail enables it to breathe air from the surface while working submerged in several inches of water. The tail is hollow and has special hair-like spikes at the tip which help hold it on the surface film. Reaumur, the great French naturalist, gave this curious larva the name of "the rat-tailed maggot," a name that has stuck to this day.

AN INSECT'S CIRCULATION SYSTEM is far different from our own. The lifestream of these small creatures, unlike our own, does not flow through veins and arteries. It moves through the open spaces of the insect's body and bathes the tissues directly. Usually the blood of an insect is colorless or has a greenish or straw-colored

37

tinge. In immature insects, the blood forms a higher percentage of the body weight than in the adults. It makes up from 25 to 30 per cent of the weight of a larval honeybee and as much as 40 per cent of the weight of a caterpillar. In the adult cockroach, no more than 5 or 6 per cent of the body weight is blood. On exposure to air, insect blood oxidizes and turns black. The fluid is slightly acid. A peculiarity of the blood of a honeybee larva is that it apparently never clots.

The heart which forces the blood through an insect is a relatively simple affair. It is a hollow chamber which extends from the head of the creature backward into the abdomen. When this muscular sac is filled with blood, a steady wave of contraction passes forward along it. The blood is forced out the front end, bathing the brain first and then flowing backward along the open channels of the body cavity. At the end of each contraction the muscles of the heart relax. This permits the blood to rush back in and the process to begin again. The rate of the heartbeats varies with the temperature. In hot weather an insect's pulse speeds up. Sometimes, amazingly, an insect heart reverses itself and beats backwards. Because it is a single tube, and not a series of chambers, it apparently makes little difference whether the organ empties the blood out of one end or the other.

In addition to the main heart, there are auxiliary pulsating organs in many insects. They operate quite independently of the heart. The familiar back-swimmers of ponds and streams have such pumps in their legs. Other insects have them in various parts of their bodies. In the housefly, they are in the wings; in the sphinx moth, in the thorax.

Because an insect is cold-blooded, the auxiliary pumps, like the main heart, operate faster or slower according to the position of the mercury. On a hot day all the body processes of an insect speed up. The smaller the animal, the greater the proportion of body surface to mass. This increases the relative amount of surface from which heat can be dissipated. Consequently, insects of necessity must be cold-blooded creatures. If they were warm-blooded, the heat would radiate away too rapidly when there was a drop in temperature.

AN INSECT WALKS in a manner that is unique among animals. If you possessed six legs and had to use them in walking, how would you move them? That is the problem which instinct has solved for the infinitely varied hosts of the adult insects.

The six legs are usually moved as a series of tripods, three legs at a time. The front and rear legs on one side, and the middle leg on the other, move in unison. Thus, the insect is always securely planted on the ground. It does not have to use a large number of muscles, as we do, just to maintain an erect posture. In walking, the average adult person employs a motor mechanism that weighs about eighty pounds—sixty pounds of muscles and twenty pounds of bones. Each step we take puts about 300 muscles in action. One hundred and forty-four are employed just to balance our spine and keep us upright.

Many insects use their legs in specialized ways. The common water-strider employs its forelegs to capture its prey, its oarlike middle legs to propel itself over the water, and its rear legs to guide it in the manner of a rudder. The legs of a dragonfly are held together to form a basket for scooping victims from the air. They are set so far forward on the insect's body that they are almost useless for walking. A dragonfly clings and climbs but hardly ever tries to walk. The monarch is sometimes called "the four-legged butterfly" because of a peculiarity in its use of its legs. This insect holds its forelegs against its body as a general rule and uses only its middle and rear pairs of legs for walking. Male monarchs have short atrophied legs that are virtually useless.

For a cow or horse, cat or dog, legs are used almost exclusively as a means of transportation. Among the insects, however, legs have innumerable other uses. Often they are whole tool kits. The rear legs of the bumblebee and the honeybee contain spine-ringed depressions—baskets for carrying pollen home from the fields. The forelegs of the mole cricket and the seventeen-year cicada nymph are enlarged into digging shovels. The swimming legs of the diving beetles are fringed with hairs to increase their effectiveness as oars.

Some insects use the claws on their feet to hang themselves up for a night's sleep. The praying mantis employs its spined forelegs as a trap for catching prey. The water-strider has legs with "snow-shoes" formed of hairs that help keep it from breaking through the surface film. When not in use, these hairs fold up into a slot in the insect's leg. A few moths have similar masses of hairs that open out into white "powder-puffs" just below the knees on the forelegs as a means of attracting their mates. The legs of no other living creatures have as great variety in form and uses as the legs of the insects.

AN INSECT SWIMS most frequently during its immature stages. The young dragonfly, stonefly, black fly, mosquito, and May fly, to name but a few forms, are aquatic. They spend their days beneath the surface, breathe through gills, and swim in individual ways. Diving beetles, the *Dytiscus* and *Hydrophilis*, pursue their prey underwater. Several other insects, the whirligig beetles and water-striders, for example, dart about on the surface. If dropped into the water most insects can manage to swim for a time at least. Crickets, locusts and various grasshoppers can make excellent progress through the water. A praying mantis will paddle ahead steadily in a manner that suggests a man swimming sailor-fashion. Ants, I have noticed, can swim either on their backs or face downward, according to how they fall into the water.

AN INSECT FLIES in a manner entirely different from that employed by the birds. Its wings move not in a rowing motion but in a series of elongated figure-eights. Many years ago, a European scientist attached tiny pieces of gold leaf to the tips of a wasp's wings and released the insect in sunlight. The glinting metal performed swift little figure-eights in the air. Since then, other experimenters have used smoked paper against which the tips of insect wings rubbed, and recently, high-speed motion pictures, to show that the figure-eight movement is the foundation of insect flight.

The lift of insect wings varies greatly according to the species. May flies and lacewing flies possess large and rather frail wings. These supporting surfaces are lightly loaded. On the other hand, the bumblebee and the robber fly have small and relatively heavily loaded wings. Most butterflies have large and lightly loaded supporting surfaces. Dragonflies also have excess wing area. In various experiments the wings of a dragonfly were bisected lengthwise from tip to base and the insect was able to fly just as before although it rode on wings with only 50 per cent as much supporting surface. However, when the wings were bisected half way out to the tip, so they were only half as long as they had previously been, the dragonfly was unable to remain in the air.

In flight, the wings of butterflies and the four-winged *Hymenoptera*—the bees, wasps, and flying ants—are locked together so they act as a single pair of supporting surfaces. Among dragonflies the two pairs of wings operate independently. When the smaller and frailer damselflies are in flight, their fluttering wings, operating as two separate pairs, give the impression of the hovering of a helicopter rather than the flight of an airplane. The more primitive insects have wings that operate as separate pairs; the later and more highly developed species which possess four wings use them as a single pair.

When at rest, the beetles fold their membranous hind wings beneath the hard outer sheaths. These sheaths represent a front pair of wings which have become heavily armored and have lost their power of rapid movement. In some cases the sheaths are outstretched when the beetle is in flight; in others they are folded over the abdomen when the insect takes to the air. Another variation in flying equipment is found in the true flies, the *Diptera*. They ride through the air on a single pair of membranous wings. Behind these wings are two knobbed organs called halteres, or balancers, which move rapidly while the insect is in flight. It is suggested that these balancers are the remnants of a second pair of wings which have been lost through evolution. Similar balancers, this time in front instead of behind the wings, are found in the males of the parasitic beetle, *Strepsiptera*.

The most powerful muscles in a flying insect's body naturally are those which operate the wings. Some of the gay-winged grasshoppers which hover for a short time and then drop back to earth, depending largely upon their powerful jumping legs rather than their wings to get them into the air, have only 8 per cent of their body weight devoted to wing muscles. They are relatively weak fliers. In contrast, the far-ranging dragonfly, *Aeschna*, has three times that figure, 24 per cent of its weight, devoted to wing muscles.

Many insects are superb airmen, among the finest fliers in the world of nature. They can shoot aloft, dart down, hover, go sidewise, or even fly backward. Steering is effected largely through the unequal activity of the wings on opposite sides of the body. The forewings of some butterflies can move forward and backward at will, in addition to having an up-and-down motion. In the case of the honeybee, sudden sidewise darts are accomplished by increasing the arc, or amplitude, of the wing motions on one side and decreasing them on the other. The frequency of the vibrations remain the same; only the amplitude is varied.

The speed at which the wings move depends largely upon the species. It also varies with the load being carried and the fatigue of the loaded insect. By comparing the hum of an insect with the sound of a tuning fork, in which the number of vibrations is known, scientists have been able to calculate the number of wing beats per second made by various flying insects. A honeybee, for example, moves its wings from 180 to 250 times a second; a bumblebee from 130 to 240; a wasp about 110; a housefly approximately 190; a ladybird beetle from 75 to 91; and an *Aeschna* dragonfly from 22 to 28. In some instances, notably in the case of the fly *Eristalis tenax*, the wings move more rapidly on the downstroke than on the upstroke. Among the sphinx moths the wings are often fluttered for a time until the body temperature of the insect is sixty-four degrees F. Below this temperature the sphinx moth appears unable to fly.

Once in flight, the insects move through the air at widely varying speeds. A fluttering lacewing fly will navigate the air above a garden at a drifting speed of approximately a mile and a half an hour. A laden honeybee, carrying a load of nectar equal to half its body weight, will return to the hive at a speed of about 15 miles an hour. R. J. Tillyard, the Australian dragonfly expert, once timed one of these fleet insects racing down a long valley on a windless day at a speed of a mile a minute. Some years ago one American scientist reported on rather scanty evidence that the deer botfly, *Cephenemyia pratti*, attains the fantastic speed of 818 miles an hour. Both the impossibility of determining accurately the speed of small insects and the impossibility of this specific fly ever attaining an 800-mile-an-hour pace were painstakingly demonstrated by the Nobel Prize winner, Dr. Irving Langmuir, in *Science* magazine in 1938.

The loads that insect wings support can be determined with greater accuracy than the speed the insects can make in free flight. Some species of insects have demonstrated that they are able to carry loads greater than their own body weight. Craneflies, those awkward, daddy-longlegs of the air, have large and lightly loaded wings. By trimming these wings, making them smaller and smaller, scientists have been able to produce the same effect as increasing the load carried by the insects. They found that, as might be expected, the frequency of the wing beats increased as the supporting surfaces grew smaller. As the wings were reduced from 22 millimeters to 10 and then to 5, the frequency ratio was 9:12:20. One of the largest loads supported in the air by an insect is the heavy body of the cicada. It weighs far more than does the cicada-killer wasp which flies with it on its way to its underground burrow.

AN INSECT FINDS ITS WAY, returning to its burrow—as in the case of the cicada-killer—or to its nest—as in the case of the ant, with a remarkable and often puzzling efficiency. Ants are known to follow formic acid trails laid down by the workers. "Muscular memories," the ability to take the opposite turns when going home over a winding trail, have been advanced to explain the return of ants and other ground insects. In the case of honeybees, Dr. Karl von Frisch has shown, the insects can see polarized light and employ it in finding their way. On occasions, an ant will make a "bee line" for home at the end of a rambling expedition in search of food. The sense of orientation, in such instances, appears based on a number of factors.

The flying wasp, on the other hand, appears to depend largely upon eyesight in finding its way home. Phil and Nellie Rau, the field entomologists of Kirkwood, Missouri, have shown by numerous ingenious experiments that such insects follow landmarks. Another research worker found that when he cut off a bush beside a digger wasp's burrow and planted it some yards away, the returning insect flew directly to the bush and not to the hole. It was using the bush as a guiding landmark and was thrown completely off the track when the marker was moved.

That still other little-understood factors may play their part in the ability of insects to find their way over wide stretches of country is demonstrated by the long migration flights of certain species, especially some of the butterflies.

AN INSECT MIGRATES, in some instances, over a distance of more than 1000 miles. The most celebrated migrant is the monarch butterfly of North America. Each autumn, flocks which sometimes number untold millions begin moving steadily southward. Some of these insects travel from as far north as Hudson Bay to the Gulf States of the South. They winter there and the following spring some of the insects return northward again. The long migration south is never made by the same butterflies on two successive falls.

Dragonflies and other insects totaling several hundred species are known to make migrations either regularly or sporadically. The painted lady moves south from Europe across the Mediterranean to northern Africa in the autumn and returns north across the Mediterranean in the spring. These frail insects flutter across hundreds of miles of water, flying both night and day. They appear in the light of ships steaming across the Mediterranean. They come from the darkness on one side of the vessel and disappear out of the light on the other side, often flying straight as the proverbial string toward a distant and unseen shore. How do they keep on their course through the hours of darkness and when flying out of the sight of landmarks? That remains one of the many unsolved mysteries of entomology. The possibility that they are guided by the electromagnetic currents of the earth has been advanced as an hypothesis but it still requires definite demonstration and proof.

AN INSECT COMMUNICATES with its fellows by means of sounds, lights, odors, touch, and other methods, some of them comparatively little understood. The fireflies signal each other by means of the luminous portions of their abdomens. Ants tap antennae on antennae, touching and rubbing them in so many different ways that one imaginative German scientist actually compiled an "Ant Dictionary," giving his version of the meaning of the different taps. The death-watch beetle, pounding its horny head against the roof of its wooden tunnel, signals to its mate. Swarming honeybees, when they settle in a golden cluster upon a bush or tree, open scent glands and send out an odor which calls the remaining insects from the air to the close-packed mass.

The language of the bees has been studied more closely than the communication system of any other insect. This is largely due to the work of Dr. Karl von Frisch, the noted Austrian research biologist. By marking hundreds of bees from a colony, he was able to identify the individual insects and follow the activity of each. The results of these investigations, extending over a period of more than twenty years, are contained in his book, *The Dancing Bees*.

When a worker finds a rich source of nectar in the fields, Dr. Von Frisch discovered, it performs a tripping little dance on the comb within the hive. Other workers crowd around it. If the nectar is less than 100 yards from the hive, the scout engages in a round dance; if it is farther away, it performs a more elaborate tail-wagging dance. The first sends the bees scattering in search of flowers near the hive that have the same perfume as that given off by the body

45

of the returning scout. But the tail-wagging dance provides more definite directions. Over and over again, the dancer turns in a half-circle in one direction, then makes a straight-line run with its abdomen waggling vigorously from side to side. Then it circles in the opposite direction and repeats the straight-line run. It is this tail-wagging run, the scientist eventually demonstrated, that gives other bees a "compass course" on which to fly to reach the nectar.

The sun is the great landmark in the sky used by the honeybees. If the run is straight up the comb, it signifies the food lies directly toward the sun. If it is straight down the comb, it indicates the nectar lies directly away from the sun. If it is at an angle to one side or the other of a straight line, it shows what angle toward or away from the sun the foraging bees should head. The scout does not lead the other bees back. It sends them, with definite directions where to go. Because honeybees can see polarized light that is invisible to our eyes, they are able to determine the position of the sun even when it is obscured by clouds if they can see one small portion of clear sky.

As long as there are insufficient workers visiting the flowers that the scout has discovered, each returning worker performs a similar tail-wagging dance, attracting additional workers to the spot. But when the nectar begins to give out, the dancing stops. No new workers are attracted and wasted effort is avoided. By means of this silent system of communication, honeybees regulate efficiently their activities afield.

AN INSECT REMEMBERS, usually, for only a relatively short period of time. Bees, and some of the far-ranging hunting wasps and ants, have the best memories of all. The place-memories of these insects are particularly good. A digger wasp will return from a mile away to the entrance of a burrow only half an inch in diameter. At the American Museum of Natural History, Dr. T. C. Schneirla has demonstrated the maze-learning ability of certain ants. On the other hand, flies seem to have no memories at all. One was seen returning again and again to a spot of danger where it had

46

narrowly escaped death at the hands of a hidden praying mantis. Cockroaches have shown an ability to learn and remember—but for a shorter period than bees and wasps.

AN INSECT SLEEPS in many different places and positions. Some robber flies "hang themselves up" for the night by means of the claws on their feet. Wasps often bite into the stem of a plant and, with their mandibles locked in position, stretch out at right angles to the stem and, with their legs dangling, fall asleep. In this position they remain through the hours of darkness. Dragonflies and butterflies usually seek shelter for the night in dense stands of vegetation. Some insects remain in the open, clinging to bark or goldenrod blooms. Others sometimes enter flowers which close at night, such as poppies, and find shelter. Not only are they thus protected from the damp but the temperature within such a closed bloom is usually slightly higher than that of the air outside.

I once found scores of bumblebees bedded down for the night in the crevices of the bark of a scarlet oak. Usually, when a bumblebee does not return to the nest during summer nights, it sleeps clinging to the underside of a leaf. This habit of bees of hanging back downward from leaves gave rise to the ancient belief that this is done to prevent dew from collecting on their wings and thus preventing them from flying when morning comes. Both small moths and some of the conehead grasshoppers often thrust their heads into curled leaves or places where the stem of a plant and a broad leaf join and there, with their heads completely hidden, go to sleep.

If you watch an ant which has been asleep for some time awaken, you will frequently see it stretch and open its jaws in a very human kind of yawn before it takes up the tasks of the day. Many insects are given to taking short cat-naps during daylight hours. I have come upon ants, wasps, bumblebees and other insects sound asleep in broad daylight. At night, some insects sleep far more soundly than others. The bedtime as well as the rising time of different insects runs through a wide range. Bumblebees are up early and

47

work late, and sometimes I have come upon the green darner dragonfly, *Anax junius*, still hawking about over mosquito infested marshlands when there was hardly light enough to see.

AN INSECT RESPONDS TO TEMPERATURE CHANGES in many ways. Being cold-blooded, it depends for its body temperature on the warmth or cold of the surrounding air. A drop in temperature slows down its activity; a rise in the mercury speeds it up. Like the chemical reaction in a test tube, the activity of the insects invariably speeds up or slows down as they are heated or cooled. Ants run more rapidly on a hot day; caterpillars bite out mouthfuls of leaf tissue at an increased tempo; robber flies dart after their prey with added alertness. Even the development of immature insects is speeded up when the weather is hot.

One summer when the Harvard astronomer, Dr. Harlow Shapley, was working at the Mount Wilson Observatory in California, he became interested in timing the speed of running ants. He found that their speed was so exactly proportional to the position of the mercury that he could tell the temperature almost exactly at any time by noting the pace of the insects. A rise of the thermometer from fifty degrees F. to one hundred degrees increased the speed of the ants over the mountain rocks fifteen times. By holding a cardboard over the line of march, Dr. Shapley found that ants entering the cooler shaded portion of the trail responded more quickly to the change in temperature than a thermometer did.

The very delicate temperature sense of the ants is demonstrated in another way. They always seem to place their brood in the best positions in the nest for utilizing the warmth of the earth and of stones. The exact location and the nature of the organs which give the ant this temperature sense are still unknown.

Other insects have become noted for a similar sensitiveness. The snowy tree cricket is the most famous of them all. It has been given the nickname of "The Temperature Cricket." The fiddling of the males increases or decreases its tempo with every slightest change in the position of the mercury. Years ago, scientists worked out a

48

formula for discovering the temperature by counting the number of chirps a minute produced by a singing snowy tree cricket. If you divide that number by four and add forty, the result indicates the temperature in Fahrenheit degrees.

A number of insects are able to increase or decrease their body temperatures by changing their position in relation to the rays of the sun. On cool mornings, grasshoppers often place themselves at right angles to the sun's rays in order to get additional heat. A locust native to Palestine is able to increase or decrease its internal temperature three degrees by altering its position on the ground. A scientist found that the temperature of the insect, when resting parallel to the rays, was seventy degrees. A few minutes later, when the locust was perched with its body at right angles to the rays, its temperature was seventy-three degrees.

AN INSECT RESPONDS TO LIGHT CHANGES just as it does to changes in temperature. Certain dragonflies will alight every time a drifting cloud obscures the sun. One grasshopper is so sensitive to changes in light intensity that Samuel H. Scudder found it would change from its day-tune to its twilight-tune whenever it was struck by the shadow of a passing cloud.

The attraction of the street lamp for the nocturnal moth and beetle is proverbial. Those who have read Henry Thoreau's *Cape Cod* will remember his account of the way in which moths covered the windows of the lighthouse, obscuring the beams to the peril of sailors, in their desire to approach the source of the brilliance. Insects that fly into the light cannot help themselves. As Dr. George A. Dorsey puts it: "A lion can learn to lie down beside a lamb, but a moth cannot learn to let a flame alone." The insect is so constituted that the angle and intensity of the light that strikes its eyes actually affect its muscles. It turns steadily in the direction of the light source without being able to alter its course.

I remember once watching a small moth which had wandered into a lecture hall where a talk on insects was in progress. It lighted on the screen where the image of a dark, irregular central object

49

had been thrown by a lantern-slide projector. The moth walked up the screen, following the outline of the dark object, keeping to the lighter part of the image. It never entered the shaded portions but, turning this way and that like a coastwise steamer hugging an irregular shore, it climbed upward to the top of the screen.

Some insects, in contrast, are repelled by light. Termites build tubes from one timber to another so they can pass in moist darkness to their new feeding ground. A blow-fly larva will crawl away from a light in a straight line. The cockroach scuttles out of sight the instant an electric light is snapped on.

In some instances, an insect is attracted to light at one period in its life and repelled by it at another. The gold-tailed moth, for example, crawls in its larval form to the far outer tips of branches when spring comes and the buds are opening. Light attracts it upward to its food. Once it has devoured the buds at the branch-tips, the larva is repelled by light. This forces it back down the branch where other buds are opening. If, after the first buds were eaten, the insect were still attracted by light, it would be held at the stripped twig-tips and starve. By being first attracted and then repelled by the light, it is led automatically to its food.

Other factors sometimes influence the insect's response to light. An instance is found in the behavior of the cluster-flies which gather in close-packed masses on the inside of windowpanes during late autumn. When the temperature drops, these flies are repelled by light. They push and squirm until they enter buildings through cracks. Inside, where the temperature is higher, the insects are attracted to the light. They fly to windows and mass together, facing out. Under laboratory conditions, the flies can be attracted to light or repelled from it simply by raising or lowering the temperature a few degrees.

AN INSECT BEHAVES INSTINCTIVELY in most of the things it does. The life of an insect is usually so short that there is little time for learning. In order to survive, the individual has to spring full-fledged in the wisdom of instinct. It has to know virtually as much on the day it is born as on the day it dies. The young queen bumblebee or paper-making wasp makes cells, lays eggs, cares for the first-emerging of her young without instruction. She knows exactly what should be done instinctively. Hundreds of worker honeybees, without anyone in charge, produce that marvelous creation, the waxen comb, each adding a bit of wax and molding it into the structure with its jaws. The sum total of their instinctive acts is the finished comb with its innumerable hexagonal cells.

The insect is usually powerless to leave the path of instinct; it does a thing each time exactly as it did it the first time. The digger wasp must sting her prey and attach her egg in a certain manner. She must invariably leave her victim at the tunnel entrance while she makes an investigation of the interior. J. Henri Fabre removed the prey of one wasp while she was inside the tunnel and placed it some feet away. A prolonged hunt followed before she found it. She dragged it back to the burrow and left it while she made her trip of investigation. Fabre again removed the prey. Forty times he did this and the result was always the same. Each time she left the insect she had paralyzed outside the burrow while she made sure all was well inside. It was impossible for her to vary her instinctive behavior.

If a moth-caterpillar is interrupted in the middle of spinning its cocoon and is placed in a new location, it will not begin again at the beginning but will always go on from where it left off. If the egg of a digger wasp is removed from one of the buried insects while she is stocking a burrow, the wasp will not lay another egg, although no larva will ever hatch to consume the insects she is bringing in. She has laid her egg and that step in the instinctive chain is past; she continues to bring in additional insects and then carefully seals up the burrow. One action stimulates another in the complicated behavior of such insects. They follow the path of a definite sequence of events which cannot be altered.

A dramatic demonstration of the inability of an insect to improvise or to meet abnormal conditions was made in one of Fabre's ingenious tests. He placed a tissue-paper covering loosely around the outside of a mason-wasp's nest. The insect which emerged from the cell was equipped with such powerful jaws that it could bite its way out through the solid masonry of the nest. But when it reached the outer shell, although it was made of tissuepaper, the wasp was baffled. Nature had equipped it with the instinct to bite its way out of one prison-cell. Outside, it was normally free to fly away. With this normal condition upset—although the wasp could have snipped through the paper with a single bite of its jaws—the insect was helpless. It wandered about within the thin shell of its prison until it died.

Within the scope of their instinctive acts, however, insects are among the cleverest animals of our globe. There is a certain beetle which secretes itself in flowers visited by bees. When one of these nectar-hunters alights, the beetle attaches itself to the legs of the bee and is carried through the air to the nest where it lays its eggs. There is a small saw-fly larva that lives on pine trees. During only one instar of its life is it attacked by a parasitic wasp. And only during that one instar does it show any fear of these insects. There is an ichneumon fly which deposits its eggs on the bodies of caterpillars. In many positions the larvae are able to bite off the eggs and frustrate the attack. So the parasite waits until the caterpillar lifts a foot. Then, like a flash, the ichneumon fly darts in and deposits its egg on the sole of the foot, a place where it cannot be removed. In the world of the insects, and in the behavior of these small, short-lived creatures, instinct reaches its most striking development.

AN INSECT HAS GREAT VITALITY in spite of its small size. I have seen a praying mantis revive after being enclosed in a cyanide killing jar for more than half an hour. Some species of ants can be submerged under water for eight days and remain unharmed. Other ants can fast for the greater part of a year. Beheaded butterflies will attempt to fly. I once saw a dragonfly which had lost all of its abdomen attempting to rise into the air. A baby praying mantis can be frozen until it is stiff and apparently lifeless without being harmed. A headless worker ant remained alive for more than forty days. And, in one laboratory experiment, an immature blood-sucking bug, *Rhodnius,* was decapitated and lived for more than a year afterwards. When brains have been removed from the heads of some insects, they have continued to eat as before whenever food was placed in contact with their mouths. Among the insects, the spark of life burns on under conditions which would have extinguished it for larger and physically stronger animals.

The frailty of the insects is deceptive. Combined with it is an amazing ability to endure. Small flies, Dr. Frank E. Lutz found, can survive tremendous punishment. In the space of four hours he subjected fruit flies to a partial vacuum equivalent to the thin air seventeen miles above the earth's surface, and then returned them suddenly to normal pressure a total of twenty-four times. In spite of this treatment, which no larger animal could have endured, two of ten fruit flies not only survived but later bred and had normal descendants.

AN INSECT'S LENGTH OF LIFE under normal conditions depends largely upon its species. Life cycles vary considerably. The May fly's adult life passes swiftly; it is a matter of hours, or days at best. The seventeen-year cicada has lived for more than a decade and a half before it appears from the ground. Far more than 95 per cent of its long life span is passed as an unseen underground dweller, tunneling through the silence and darkness of the earth and sucking sap from the roots of herbaceous plants and trees.

In the northern states, most insects live only during the summer season and pass away with the first frosts of autumn. The first night of killing frost silences the insect orchestra of the crickets, katydids, and grasshoppers. Some insects have but one generation during the summer months. Others like the monarch butterfly, have two or three broods, and still others, like the rapidly multiplying aphides, have as many as thirty generations before autumn comes. That season of transition from warm to cold weather brings to a close the adult life of a host of different insects. Only a comparatively few species pass the months of cold in the adult form.

AN INSECT SURVIVES THROUGH THE WINTER, either as an individual or as a species, by the employment of innumerable stratagems and cunning tricks. The mourning cloak butterfly seeks out a hollow tree or cranny where it can lie protected during the worst of the winter weather. The monarch sails southward to sunny skies. The tiger swallowtail and the other species of *Papilio* winter as exposed chrysalises. The viceroy remains until spring as a partly grown larva within a rolled leaf. The great silk moths, the *Polyphemus, Promethea, Cecropia,* and *Luna,* all pass the winter as pupae within silken cocoons.

Crickets and grasshoppers deposit their eggs within the protection of the ground. The moth of the tent caterpillar, *Malacosoma americana,* places her eggs in a band around a twig and coats them with a varnish-like covering which protects them from rain and sleet. A protection of another kind is provided for the eggs of the praying mantis. They are surrounded by froth which solidifies into an egg-case holding at its center from 125 to 350 elongated yellow eggs.

Bumblebees and paper-making wasps depend upon fertilized queens, which hibernate over winter, to start new colonies in spring. All the other members of the populous colonies are killed by autumn frosts. The dragonflies, May flies, damselflies, and other aquatic insects remain, semiactive, as nymphs beneath the water during winter. Water-striders hibernate in trash along the banks, coming out to skate on the surface film during midwinter thaws. Mosquitoes and lacewing flies often hibernate as adults in dark corners of country cellars. The white grubs of the May beetles work downward in the ground below the frost line as winter comes, while those "upholstered worms," the woolly-bear caterpillars, hibernate curled up beneath stones and old boards.

Many of the true bugs bridge the gap between fall and spring by hibernating in grass clumps and trash piles as adults. Hundreds of hibernating chinch bugs have been taken from the lower section of a single grass clump. The eggs of insects pass the winter in many places. Those of the plant lice are attached to bark and plant tis-

54

sues; those of the angular-winged katydid are cemented in overlapping rows along the edge of a leaf or the top of a twig; those of the walking-sticks are dropped promiscuously to lie among the brown fallen leaves.

Of all the many methods of enduring through the winter, the most unusual is probably that employed by the honeybees, *Apis mellifera*. When cold weather comes, these insects gather together in a golden ball within the hive and those on the interior of the mass begin a dance which warms their bodies through the chemical reaction caused by muscular activity. The heat radiated from these dancing bees raises the temperature of the cluster and the close-packed bodies of the other bees form a sort of insulated shell which prevents rapid escape of the warmth that is produced. Throughout the months of winter, this muscular furnace raises the temperature within the hive and prevents the bees from freezing. There is sometimes more than seventy-five degrees F. difference between the center of such a cluster and that of the air outside the hive. In a continual, slow interchange, the bees on the outside of the ball work toward the center, changing places with the heated dancers. In this manner, all the bees are kept warm.

Only the great stores of golden honey in the wax cells of the hive make this muscular furnace possible. It is the fuel that keeps the insect heating plant going. Muscular activity uses up energy and without stores of food, the insects would soon wear themselves out and die. It is the labor of summer days, the nectar-gathering and honey-storing, that enables the bees to use this unique method of insuring their survival.

AN INSECT DIES, normally, from numerous causes: from overwork, from starvation, from cold, from reaching the end of its life span. A fly only a few weeks old may be proportionately as old as a man of eighty. The life-expectancy—to use an insurance term—of different insects varies with the species and the kind of life they lead. A late-autumn honeybee, entering a period of relative inactivity within the winter hive, may live for six months or more. A worker bee in the midst of the honeyflow, when nectar is everywhere and the insects are laboring at top speed from dawn to dark, may wear itself out in six weeks.

In early autumn, the hosts of the insects attain their high tide. Most of these legions, filling the weedlots and grass clumps with sound and movement, will pass in the first heavy frost. In that night of cold, their tissues freeze and life departs. The rising sun finds their myriad bodies motionless among the tangled grass and vegetation. On such a morning, there is a hush—for the insect singers suddenly are no more. Of all the ways in which the end of life comes to the insects, it is the autumn cold which brings the most sudden and widespread destruction.

In all probability, only a small percentage of the insects that reach their adult forms during the summer months live into autumn. Most are overtaken by accidents or fall victim to their innumerable enemies. The "normal" death of the insect is a sudden and violent one. Usually the female insect survives longer than the male; she has, as a rule, a longer life span. She is also normally larger than the male. The insect world is essentially a female world in which the male plays a secondary part.

* * *

Because it is almost literally true that we see only what we understand, the small and mystery-filled realm of the insects is virtually overlooked by the average person. To him, the insects are as Maeterlinck observes in *Mountain Paths:* ". . . those vague, unconscious, rudimentary and almost nameless little lives which surround us on every side and which we contemplate with eyes that are amused, but already thinking of other things, when we open our window to welcome the first hours of spring, or when we go into the gardens or the fields to bask in the blue summer days."

Because of their small size, watching the insects is like looking at a drama from a remote seat in the highest balcony of a theater. It also is like arriving in the middle of Act III. So much has gone before of which we are ignorant; so much is going on which we do not understand. Yet knowing the habits and the endowments of the insects is important in many ways.

The tremendous fertility of these tiny creatures, their ability to live on little, their record of colonizing every habitable spot, their endurance and vitality and versatility, have led many men to the conclusion that the insects may be man's chief competitor for mastery of the world. From the days of the prophet Joel with his vivid description of the locust plague beginning with the words: "A day of darkness and of gloominess, a day of clouds and thick darkness . . . ," to Dr. Leland O. Howard, for many years head of the Bureau of Entomology of the U.S. Department of Agriculture with his book *The Insect Menace*, there have been eloquent expositions of the vast potential danger of the insects.

In the United States, the greatest destruction wrought by the insects—the sweep of the boll weevil across the South from the Rio Grande, the march of the Colorado potato beetle from the Rockies to the eastern coast, the outbreaks of the chinch bug and the Hessian fly and the corn borer—has been a consequence of man's upsetting the balance of nature.

The Colorado potato beetle, for example, lived a relatively uneventful life for countless generations among the valleys of the Rocky Mountains. It fed on a wild relative of the potato vine. Until the coming of the pioneers, its numbers were comparatively few. Then settlers began planting fields of potatoes in the region. The beetles found a vast banquet table suddenly set before them, row on row. No longer did they have to hunt for sparse fare. The tribe prospered and multiplied. They spread to other fields and began their steady march to the east. At the rate of approximately eighty-five miles a year, they advanced until they reached the Atlantic Coast. Great stretches of fields, in which nothing else than potatoes were found, upset the balance of Nature and caused the rapid spread of the beetles.

Similarly, the vast cotton fields of the South automatically aided the increase of the boll weevil once it had crossed the Rio Grande. In its Mexican home, this weevil had fed mainly on scattered plants

57

of wild cotton. Like the Colorado potato beetle, its fare was sparse. But in the cotton fields which stretched mile on mile across southern states, it found itself suddenly thrown into a boll weevil's heaven. It ate its fill, waxed strong, multiplied, and, in the end, has levied the equivalent of a $120,000,000-a-year tax on the country.

In the "Bread Basket" of the Middle West, the great stretches of corn and of wheat likewise have played into the hands of the corn borer, the chinch bug, and the Hessian fly. Under natural conditions, an insect which infests a certain type of vegetation usually has to hunt for isolated plants or clumps over a comparatively wide area. Nature practices diversified farming. This is one of the factors which keep various insects in check under natural conditions. Under artificial and man-made conditions, however, certain species have become major pests because they have had provided for them ideal surroundings for their swift increase.

Another way in which the balance of nature has been upset, permitting some insects to run riot, is through the importation of plants from abroad. Insects have come in with these importations and have found themselves in new and favorable environments. The parasites which normally prey upon them and keep them in check in their native lands have been left behind.

The Japanese Beetle is an outstanding instance of the kind. Established by accident near Riverton, N.J., it has spread unchecked across several states. Sometimes the parasite which has been left behind can be imported for a "bug-eat-bug" form of biological control. Thus a ladybird beetle from Australia saved the citrus groves of California by checking the ravages of an imported scale insect. But in many instances, the parasite is upset by new conditions or the imported pest changes its mode of life under the new environment and the efforts fail.

Fortunately for man, the insect world is divided against itself. It is a realm of endless struggle, of fierce and deadly competition. The tremendous fertility of the insects is kept in hand by an elaborate system of checks and balances. It is estimated that far more than half the insects prey upon other insects. The parasite

58

that attacks one insect has a parasite which attacks it, and that secondary parasite has a tertiary parasite which preys upon it in turn. Dean Swift's lines about "bigger fleas have littler fleas on their backs to bite 'em" is sound natural history.

In any part of the country, if milkweed begins to increase, monarch butterflies appear in larger numbers. Their larvae keep the plant in check. Whenever a plague of army worms descends upon a countryside, small wasplike insects, which parasitize and kill the caterpillars, appear in vast numbers. Normally, no one species can run amuck for long without having the balance of nature assert itself. All animal and vegetable life is knit together into one vast web and each individual insect is part of the fabric.

* * *

According to its nature and habits and abilities, the insect plays its part, a part which affects to some degree the other forms of animal and plant life with which it is associated. Each species differs in its life story. In the pages that follow, lives of representative insects will be recorded in detail.

In the scientific classification of insects, entomologists are in disagreement over the number of major divisions or orders. In his *College Entomology* (1951), E. O. Essig, of the University of California, lists thirty-three orders. The 1960 edition of John Henry Comstock's *An Introduction to Entomology* gives twenty-six orders. *Insects*, the U.S. Department of Agriculture Yearbook for 1952, places the number at twenty-four. At any rate, many of these orders represent small, specialized groups of rarely encountered insects such as the *Thysanura*, the wingless bristletails, the *Corrodentia*, the book-lice, the *Mallophaga*, the bird-lice, and the *Strepsiptera*, the twisted-winged insects.

Almost all the insects the average person is likely to see belong to eleven orders. They are the *Ephemeroptera*, the *Odonata*, the *Isoptera*, the *Orthoptera*, the *Hemiptera*, the *Homoptera*, the *Neuroptera*, the *Coleoptera*, the *Lepidoptera*, the *Diptera* and the *Hymenoptera*. The insect biographies that follow indicate what life is like for members of these eleven orders.

PART III

LIVES OF
FAMILIAR INSECTS

1. THE LIFE OF
THE MAY FLY

EPHEMEROPTERA

EARLY in the summer of 1909, two men were camping on a riverbank in Missouri. About eight-thirty in the evening, one of the campers added wood to the fire and the flames leaped up. A moment later, they heard a sound as though a lighted match had been dropped into a bucket of water. It was followed by a similar sound, then others coming in quick succession. The air seemed filled with drifting raindrops. The men looked up. The stars had disappeared. In less than five minutes, the blazing campfire was completely extinguished by a living rain of innumerable May flies.

Along the banks of the St. Lawrence River during another spring, a government entomologist was following the winding road in his car when the machine was suddenly enveloped in a seeming blizzard. The air appeared to be filled with swirling snow and the ground around him was covered. Uncounted millions of May flies were sweeping over the riverbank and countryside in one vast, far-extending cloud.

At the height of a May fly emergence, piles of the dead insects will often be found beneath the street lamps of river and lake towns, piles several feet thick and three or four feet across. Along lake shores, the waves will wash such a myriad of lifeless May flies onto the beach that they form great windrows miles in length. Although the individual insects are among the frailest and most ethereal of flying creatures, their numbers are sometimes so vast that the accumulated heaps are shoveled up and hauled away in carts to fertilize fields or are piled into troughs to feed hogs. In the gaslight era in Paris, the May flies which arose in abnormal numbers from the Seine River during certain years put out the street lamps just as they extinguished the fire of the Missouri campers.

One of the most vivid descriptions of such an emergence is contained in the twelfth memoir of the sixth volume of the *Naturelle Historie des Animales,* by the eminent French scientist René A. F. Reaumur. It relates to events near Paris in the summer of 1738.

"I resolved to attend to the emergence of the fly," he records, "and . . . on the 19th of August, three hours before sunset, I took my boat to examine the banks of the Marne and Seine. At about eight o'clock, the coming on of evening and the flashes of an approaching thunderstorm caused me to return into an arm of the Marne which washes the stairs leading from my garden.

"The exclamations of my gardener, who had gone to the foot of the stairs, attracted my attention. I then saw a sight beyond all expectation. The Ephemerae filled the air like the snowflakes of a dense snowstorm. The steps were covered to a depth of two, three, and even four inches. A tract of water five or six feet across was completely hidden, and as the floating insects slowly drifted away, others took their place. Several times I was obliged to retreat to the top of the stairs from the annoyance caused by the Ephemerae which dashed into my face and got into my eyes, mouth, and nose.

"The person who held the light had a bad time of it; in a few moments he was covered with the flies which came in all directions as if to overwhelm him. The luminous sphere about the light was crossed at all angles by the orbits of the circling insects, which, after performing one or two revolutions, fell to the earth. Heaped one upon the other, and unable to move, they die by inches, the last survivors perhaps seeing the rising of the sun."

It is the briefness of this adult life, even more than the enormous numbers of the insects which sometimes appear, that makes the May fly so widely known. Its scientific name is derived from the creatures of Greek mythology, the Ephemerides, which lived but a day. Throughout the world, the May fly stands in literature as a symbol for the swift passing of life, for the transitory nature of existence. Found in many lands and surprisingly far into northern latitudes, these insects since the days of Aristotle have aroused the interest of both poets and naturalists. North America has 550 species of May flies. In the world there are about 1500 species.

The May fly is an insect of many names. In angler's entomology, these insects are known variously as shad flies, willow flies, cisco flies, river flies, trout flies, eel flies, day flies, spinners, drakes, duns, cocktails, dotterels, mackerels, and cob flies. French anglers refer to the May flies as the manna of the fish. Some of the finest of the artificial dry-flies for catching trout—the spinners, duns, and drakes—are patterned after the May fly. On the American side of Lake Erie, May flies are referred to as "Canadian soldiers"; on the Canadian side, they are called "Yankee soldiers."

Fossil May flies, descending from Devonian times, show that the prehistoric ancestors of the *Ephemeroptera* were gigantic in comparison with the modern insects. But their relationship can be told at a glance. For millions of years, the May flies have been following the peculiar pattern of their existence.

This cycle of life begins with the underwater hatching of the eggs which have been deposited by the females. Out of the eggs creep the minute nymphs of the May flies. Depending upon their species, they take up their life of feeding and growing in varied locations. For a year, and in some cases for as long as three years, they live underwater, breathing through gills and obtaining oxygen from the water in the manner of a fish. The tracheal gills of a May fly nymph extend out from either side of its body, based on as many as seven of the abdominal segments. To protect the gills from becoming clogged with fine silt, some species of immature May flies have a protecting cover over them. It is formed of inter-lacing fringes of bristles.

The habitat of a growing May fly ranges all the way from rushing mountain torrents to the still water of landlocked and tiny ponds. At a glance, an expert can tell the sort of a home from which a given May fly nymph has come. Those that cling to rocks in swift streams are more flattened than the nymphs that dwell in quiet waters. One species, found nowhere except in whitewater streams, has flattened gills that lie against the surface of a stone, producing an oval attachment-disk that gives the insect a limpet-like grip on the rock and prevents the wild rush of water from carrying it away.

Other special adaptations permit different species to survive under a wide variety of conditions. One of the commonest of the American May flies, *Hexagenia*, burrows in the mud of pond-bottoms and river beds. Its forelegs are specially flattened to form scooping shovels and its jaws appear as projecting tusks. By using these two tools alternately, it tunnels its way along like an under-water mole.

The minings of these immature insects sometimes can be seen as a vast number of tiny holes at the margins of streams. From many of these burrows, the threadlike tails of the May fly nymphs project. Pull out one of the nymphs and deposit it on an open space and it will burrow into the earth, out of sight, in an amazingly short lapse of time. Numerous other species of nymphs spend their days sprawling in the silt or climbing among the submerged masses of aquatic vegetation.

All of these nymphs are engaged, after their individual fashion, in feeding on the underwater pastures of the pond or river or lake which they inhabit. In the main, their food consists of microscopic plants and almost invisible particles of vegetable matter. The mouthparts of a May fly nymph are specially adapted for rasping off minute sections of decaying plants and for raking in masses of diatoms.

Chirotonetes, the May fly which is familiarly known as the "White-Gloved Howdy," has a peculiar feeding method of its own. It is a dweller of the tumbling water of swift and stony brooks. Here it clings to a rock, holding its forelegs up to catch food that is carried past by the rushing current. These forefeet are equipped with fringes of long hairs. Held thus together, the fringed feet of the insects form a basket-seine which scoops edible minutiae from the water. In contrast to the sluggish movements of many of the sprawling nymphs, the "Howdy" is capable of making swift rushes —dashes performed almost with the speed of a minnow.

The feeding of the May fly nymphs often comes to a sudden end. They have a host of enemies ever on the alert. Fish dart at them with open jaws. Dragonfly and stonefly nymphs stalk them through the underwater pastures. Backswimmers and diving beetles pursue them. Frogs and water birds and carnivorous salamanders take their toll.

In the turmoil of spring freshets and floods, the pounding of ice and the rolling of stream-bed stones crush many of the nymphs. The pools in which they dwell sometimes dry up and they are left to suffocate in the open air. Some become fatally entangled in the blanket algae. Sinuous-bodied, almost microscopic punkie larvae come from filaments of the algae to feed on new-born May fly nymphs. But of all these dangers, the one that is ever-present and paramount is the constant menace of foraging fish. May fly nymphs are the chief food of the white bass and several other fresh-water game fish. When the adults are emerging, they are the favorite fare of trout. The stomach content of seven rainbow trout revealed that 34 per cent of their diet consisted of this one kind of insect.

The May fly was one of the first insects to be studied in the modern, scientific manner. The great Dutch naturalist of the seventeenth century, Jan Swammerdam, in his monumental *Biblia*

67

Naturae recorded a detailed and remarkably exact history of the life of the May fly. He obtained his information by incredibly toilsome methods. A contemporary of his has given us a vivid picture of this pioneer explorer with a microscope at his work:

"His labors were superhuman. Through the day he observed incessantly, and at night he described and drew what he had seen. By six o'clock in the morning in summer he began to find enough light to enable him to trace the minutiae of natural objects. He was hard at work till noon, in full sunlight, and bareheaded, so as not to obstruct the light; and his head streamed with profuse sweat. His eyes, by reason of the blaze of light and microscopic toil, became so weakened that he could not observe minute objects in the afternoon, though the light was not less bright than in the morning, for his eyes were weary, and could no longer perceive readily."

In his quaint description of the May fly nymphs, Swammerdam observes that they were the most "mild, gentle and innocent" insects he had ever encountered. In whatever manner they were treated, they remained "calm and peaceful." As a matter of fact, the May fly nymph has no equipment for offense or defense except its agility and protective covering. It survives, as a species, by virtue of its numbers. As the underwater weeks advance, the numbers of the May fly nymphs decrease; but there are always thousands left when emergence time arrives.

In some species, this comes within a few weeks after the eggs are laid. The life cycle of one species, *Callibaetis*, lasts only six weeks. It has more than one generation during the summer season. In other species, as many as three years pass over the underwater world before emergence begins. The nymphal life of such May flies, longer than the entire lives of numerous small mammals, is sometimes a thousand times as long as the adult existence of the insect.

During this growing period, the insect molts again and again— in some cases, twenty times. Toward the end of its aquatic life, it develops wing-pads. Their appearance serves notice that close at hand is that sudden and dramatic change from gill-breathing to air-breathing, from dim underwater ways to the world of the open sky.

The swiftness with which this transformation is made has amazed every observer who has been fortunate enough to witness it. The immature insect creeps up the bank or rises to the surface of the water. Its nymphal skin splits down the back. Then, as Reaumur puts it, we cannot take our arm from the sleeve of a coat more readily than the May fly extricates its abdomen, wings, legs, and long tail-filaments. One scientist, who repeatedly timed the operation, found that not more than ten seconds elapse from the time the skin cracks until the winged insect flies away.

There is good reason for this haste. The seconds while the transformation is taking place, especially if it occurs at the water's surface, are perilous ones. Water-striders sprint toward them and fish, shooting to the surface, gorge themselves by snapping up the helpless insects. Trout, bass, and pickerel sometimes leap into the air and seize them as they rise on the wing. So anxious are the May flies to leave the element which so long has been their home that they sometimes take wing with the nymphal skin trailing behind them, still clinging to the long tail-filaments.

Another reason for the hurried emergence of the May flies is that numerous species transform amid swift-running waters. At Niagara Falls, May flies cast their skins and take to the air in the foaming torrent that is pouring over the very brink of the falls. Observers have seen swallows dart into the mist and come out with their bills filled with the insects.

Once the process of transformation begins, the insect itself is wholly powerless to stop it. When Reaumur tried to halt the change halfway through, in order to see how the wings are folded in their sheaths, he discovered that crushing the insect's head or thrusting it alive into alcohol was unavailing. In each case, the May fly completed its transformation before it perished.

Perhaps it is the May fly's need for swift emergence from the water which accounts for the fact that it alone among all the insects known to science has a second molt after it attains its winged adult form. When it leaves its nymphal skin, it is clad in a thin membranous pellicle which is shed in a later and final molt. In some species, this membrane is shed after a few minutes of quiescence; in other species, two days or more may elapse. Before it sheds this final sheath, the May fly is known to science as a sub-imago; afterwards it is an imago. In England, the dull-colored sub-imagos are called "duns" and the imagos are referred to as "spinners."

These adults spend their first hours resting, clinging to foliage. The frail legs of some species are almost too weak to support them. They do not walk or run or climb. They merely cling. With forelegs thrust far ahead of them; with veined, transparent wings folded vertically over their backs like a butterfly; with long threadlike tail-filaments trailing behind, they remain motionless. Their numbers are sometimes so vast that they bend down the branches of bushes and streamside willows with their weight. They waste no time hunting food. A May fly never eats. For so many generations has this been true that the insects have only the atrophied remains of mouth and stomach. Seen side-view, the May fly looks "weak chinned." Its mouthparts have degenerated through countless generations of disuse. The adult life of the May fly is so fleeting that nourishment is not needed.

Only one event remains on the insect's calendar. It is the grand finale of its winged hours, the event which brings life to a close: the mating and the laying of the eggs from which the next generation of nymphs will hatch.

One of the most bizarre sights in the insect world is the vast, spectacular nuptial dance of the adult May flies. The males gather in immense swarms. They rise and fall like bits of thistledown drifting on the breeze. And the females come to meet them in the air. According to their species, the May flies maneuver this way and that. They pass and repass their companions in the dance. At times, they rise and fall in unison. When the females slip into the swarm of males, they, too, take up the dance. This continues until some male rushes suddenly upon a female and seizes her. They fly away together and the dance goes on.

Thus, untold numbers of the May flies engage in the swarming which climaxes their strange existence. Some species dance only on warm and sunny days, performing their aerial evolutions above grassy meadows close to water. Others dance only at twilight. Still others continue far into the night, swirling and eventually falling to the ground at every point of brilliant illumination. The males comprise most of the weaving, drifting dancers. Only a few ever have a chance to mate with the less-numerous females.

During this nuptial dance, misfortune overtakes many of the insects. Sunset dragonflies dart among them. Swallows skim through the living clouds of the dancers. Bullfrogs, squatting beside streams, wait for descending May flies to come within reach. And, beneath old bridges, the orb-webs of the spiders ensnare thousands of the insects. Some collectors who specialize in May flies make it a habit to examine the webs of such spiders each day during spring and summer months. In this way, they keep track of the successive emergences of the different species of the insects.

When mating is over, the females return again to the water, risking the hazard of ravenous fish to lay their eggs. Although most species of May flies probably lay fewer, some females are known to deposit 1000 or more eggs. Reaumur counted 350 in a single gelatinous clump no more than a quarter of an inch in length. In three different ways, the eggs of the May fly are placed in the water. Some females drop clusters of eggs. Others dip the end of their abdomens in the water and let the current wash away a few eggs at a time. Some of these are flattened so they separate and drift over a wider area in descending to the bed of the stream. The third method of depositing the eggs is the most spectacular. The insect breaks through the surface film and crawls under-water in order to attach her eggs to the sides of submerged stones.

A female of the genus *Baetis* was observed by Dr. Ann Haven Morgan, of Mt. Holyoke College, in the midst of this dangerous expedition. The insect alighted on a rock that projected above

71

the flowing water of the stream. Walking to the protected, down-stream side of the stone, the May fly appeared to wrap its wings about its abdomen. Then it thrust its head under-water and walked downward along the submerged portion of the stone. Several min-utes passed while she searched for the right location. This found, she braced her legs, bent the tip of her abdomen downward and began attaching the minute white eggs to the face of the rock. Like a slow-motion picture of a man mowing with a scythe, she moved the tip of her abdomen with a pendulum motion, at the end of each movement taking a step ahead to permit the depositing of another row of eggs. When a series of these rows had been com-pleted, she ceased her work and clambered up the face of the rock into the open air.

The tiny eggs that the May flies deposit have innumerable forms. Beneath the microscope, some look like the pods of wild cucumbers; others are covered with scattered craters and finger-like projections. Still others have strings which are coiled like springs on the outside of the eggs, each with a terminal disk or sucker which will adhere to rocks or pebbles or even to the smooth surface of glass. One species of May fly deposits eggs that have two strings, each many times the length of the egg, at either pole. A thick gelatinous coating on other eggs glues them to the first object they strike. The ad-hesive coating of still other eggs seems to collect fine microscopic particles of silt and organic matter from the water as they descend, thus providing a camouflage that prevents their being recognized by predators.

For predators of many kinds dine on May fly eggs. Caddis worms consider them a delicacy, as do snails and other aquatic creatures. In addition, other hazards confront the deposited eggs. During freshets, they are buried in silt and mud. At other times, flood waters carry them ashore and strand them high and dry when the overflow subsides. Out of the innumerable eggs, however, enough always escape the surrounding dangers to provide the generation of another year.

At the end of the egg-laying, the females are exhausted. With wings outspread, they float on the surface of the water. While

72

a few species live for two or three days, and in some instances even longer, others have an adult existence that is encompassed by a few hours' time. The May fly's life is culminated by the briefest winged state known among the insects. "A May fly may arise at noon from the water that cradled it," J. Arthur Thomson observes, "and by sundown its aerial dance of love may be over and its lifeless body be floating on the surface of the pool."

This life that ends, oftentimes, on the day that it begins, has long stirred the thoughtful imagination of philosophers. Goethe set down his conclusion that: "Nature holds a couple of draughts from the cup of love to be fair payment for the pains of a lifetime." Of all the philosophical writings on the May fly, probably the most widely known is Benjamin Franklin's satire, *The Ephemera: An Emblem of Human Life*. It was written in France, in 1778, after witnessing—exactly forty years after Reaumur—the emergence of the May flies along the river Seine. I will end this record of the swiftly passing life of this insect with part of the soliloquy which Franklin reported he overheard as he passed a bush on which sat a venerable May fly, an insect which had lived four hundred and twenty minutes.

" 'It was the opinion of the learned philosophers of our race,' the mayfly said, 'that this vast world could not itself subsist more than eighteen hours; and I think there was some foundation for that opinion, since by the apparent motion of the great luminary that gives life to all nature, and which in my time has evidently declined considerably toward the ocean at the end of our earth, it must then finish its course, be extinguished in the waters that surround us, and leave the world in cold and darkness, necessarily producing universal death and destruction.

" 'I have lived seven of those hours, a great age. . . . How very few of us continue so long! By the course of nature, though still in health, I cannot expect to live above seven or eight minutes longer. What now avails all my toil and labor, the political struggles I have been engaged in for the good of my compatriot inhabitants of this bush, or my philosophical studies for the benefit of our race in general? Alas! Art is long and life is short. . . .' "

73

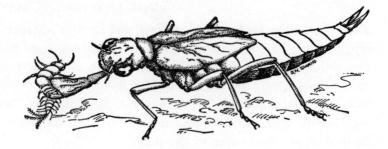

2. THE LIFE OF
THE DRAGONFLY

THE UNDERWATER realm of the immature May fly is also the home of the dragonfly nymph. No other inhabitant of that drowned world of silt and submerged vegetation and bright green algae is more fantastic than is this squat, mud-colored, water-breathing carnivore. It is far removed from Swammerdam's "innocent and peaceful" May flies. The, dragonfly nymph is a bloodthirsty ogre, stalking endlessly for living prey.

If you bring one to an aquarium and watch it closely, you can see its bizarre method of hunting, its use of a weapon of offense that is unknown elsewhere in natural history. On its six spindly legs, it will move sluggishly about, creeping along the mud or clambering slowly amid the miniature forests of the underwater plants. Then, when within reach of some small prey, it pauses, an arm seems to dart out from beneath its body and then flick back again between its forelegs. The prey has disappeared. Again

74

and again, you see this performance repeated. Finally, you are able to observe exactly what is taking place.

. The arm, in reality, is an underlip—an amazing, jointed underlip half as long as the rest of the insect's body. It functions much as your arm does when you extend it with the palm of your hand held upwards. The middle joint of the underlip operates in the manner of your elbow. The end of the lip, represented by your hand, has only two "fingers" in the form of sharp claws, curved inward. These claws grip the victim which is then dragged swiftly back to the mouth of the nymph. The jointed "arm" folds back under the body of the nymph while the "hand" rests like a mask over the lower part of the insect's face.

Using this swiftly extended lowerlip, an immature dragonfly which I once observed in action snapped up mosquito wigglers from infested waters at the rate of more than a score a minute. Both as nymphs and as adults, dragonflies are friends of man through their destruction of mosquitoes. They gobble them down as wigglers when they are nymphs and they snatch them out of the air as flying mosquitoes when they are adult dragonflies. Sometimes, a dragonfly catches so many mosquitoes there will be 100 or more in its mouth at one time. R. J. Tillyard found one dragonfly which had such a mass of mosquitoes in its mouth that it could not close its jaws. A familiar name of the dragonfly is well merited: The Mosquito Hawk.

But to return to the underwater nymph. Alarm it and you will see it perform a second surprising act. With its legs lifted from the mud, it shoots forward like a miniature rocket leaving a swirl of water behind. It does, indeed, use a kind of rocket propulsion in these sudden spurts of speed. The immature insect breathes through gills which are located within the body at the lower end of its food canal. The water is drawn in and rhythmically expelled again. When alarmed, the nymph expels the water in a sudden jet which drives it forward rocketwise for several inches. I have seen an alarmed insect, when only partly submerged in an aquarium, shoot back drops of water more than twenty inches.

75

The nymphs of the smaller and frailer dragonflies, the damsel-flies, use a different method of propelling themselves forward. Their gills are external. They extend like long feathers to the rear. By moving these feather-gills from side to side in a sculling motion, the nymphs drive themselves ahead. Thus, both the large dragon-flies and the smaller damselflies combine breathing with a means of forward propulsion.

Many nymphs among the 412 species of dragonflies found in North America and the 4870 species known to the world complete their underwater life in one year; others, however, take two years and some even as long as five years. All during this time they consume nothing but animal food. Everything from protozoa to tadpoles make up the diet of the nymph. Tiny minnows fall prey to the grasping underlip of these immature insects. In one instance, 50,000 young fish were placed in a pond swarming with dragonfly nymphs. This effort to stock the water was a complete failure. Only about fifty of the fish survived; more than 49,000 were devoured by the dragonfly nymphs. The ever-hungry nymphs are cannibals as well as carnivores. When the opportunity permits, they stalk their own kind as readily as they do the smaller aquatic creatures of pond and stream. A nymph has even been seen climbing up out of the water on a plant to attack a helpless dragonfly emerging, soft and rumpled, from its nymphal skin.

What would happen to one of these voracious creatures if it should lose the use of the clawed underlip upon which it depends for its livelihood? The answer has been supplied by a laboratory experiment. In 1939, an American entomologist removed the under-lip from a nymph in an aquarium and watched to see what would happen. The young dragonfly developed an entirely new method of capturing its prey. At first it stalked catwise toward some smaller insect, depending upon getting close enough to grasp it with its jaws. Later, it developed a leaping technique. When it got as close as possible, it aimed itself for its victim and, with a sudden jet of expelled water, shot forward, snapping at its prey with its jaws. In this way, the insect sustained itself for nearly a month.

76

Dragonfly nymphs have many peculiarities. They sometimes play 'possum, feigning death, when they are captured. If certain nymphs are grasped by one foot, they have the ability to shed part of their own legs and thus escape. Instead of having the muscles attached directly to the femur, these nymphs have them attached to a membrane which holds the femur in position. By suddenly contracting the muscles, the nymph breaks the membrane and the lower part of the leg is discarded with scarcely any loss of blood. This astonishing feat saves the lives of many nymphs both when they are in the grip of an enemy and when they have become hopelessly entangled in underwater vegetation or strands of algae.

Dr. Elsie B. Klots tells of another peculiarity of dragonfly nymphs. During an unusually hot Arizona night, while staying at the Boyce Thompson Arboretum for Plant Research, at Superior, Arizona, she noticed that dragonfly nymphs near a reservoir dam were coming in great numbers into the circle of light cast by a gasoline lantern. A later test proved that the beam of an electric flashlight was sufficient to bring the nymphs swimming or hurrying along the bottom, attracted by the illumination.

That nymphs have the ability to learn from experience is illustrated by the fact that they can be trained, in an aquarium, to come for food.

While the nymphs hunt endlessly for prey, they, in turn, are hunted by many enemies. The *Dytiscus* water beetles and the hungry trout wreak havoc among them. Chief aids in escaping their enemies are the nymphs' inconspicuous color and form. Some of the immature dragonflies burrow into the mud; others hang, usually head-downward, from submerged aquatic plants; still others sprawl on muddy pond-bottoms; while some species spend their days among the riffles of swift-flowing brooks and streams.

In all of these habitats, they gradually alter in form and size, molting repeatedly—in some species as many as fifteen times— until they reach maturity. During these successive molts many changes occur. The number of six-sided lenses in the compound eyes increases. The antennae gain new joints. The legs of many species lose their hairiness. Wing-pads appear on the thorax, or mid-body. Such changes are the prelude to the greatest and most dramatic change of all, the transformation from the muddy, water-world nymph to the colorful, glinting, winged creature of the air.

Creeping up out of the water, the nymph clings, head upward, to some solid support. Twelve hooks, two on each foot, secure it in position. Here it rests for some time while unseen activity takes place within its body. The outward evidence of this internal action is a rent which lengthens down the skin along the top of the thorax. The back of the adult insect forces itself upward, widening this rent. When the head and thorax are free, the insect draws its legs out of their hard sheaths, arching itself backward to aid in the process. At this point, if the helpless adult should fall into the water—which has been its home for many months—it would drown. It has ceased to be a water-breathing creature.

Sometimes an emerging dragonfly will remain for a quarter of an hour almost motionless, while its limbs harden, before it attempts to pull itself completely free from its nymphal skin. The last part of its body to appear is the tip of its abdomen. The wings, folded like a fan up until now, begin to expand. Blood, pumped from the insect's body, forces them open rapidly. The fluid runs through the veins of the wings like water flowing through pipes. When first expanded, the glistening wings are unfit for flight. They have to harden before they can be used. At first they are held vertically over the back of the insect. After an hour or so, they are lowered to the familiar horizontal position. Sometimes as many as five hours elapse before the wings are in condition for flight.

It is during this period of motionless waiting that the brilliant colors of the dragonfly grow in intensity. When the damp and disheveled insect first works its way out of its nymphal skin, its colors are faint. Gradually, their brilliance and distinctness increase. The blood which is pumped into the wings to expand them imparts a beautiful iridescence which disappears when the wings are completely dry. The colors of the dragonflies range through

78

the rainbow. They are lavender, ultramarine, coppery brown, apple green, azure blue, scarlet, crimson, lilac, cerulean blue, blood red, and ivory white. They vie with the butterflies and moths in beauty of form and color. And in the air, with their speed and grace, they have no equal among the insects.

A dragonfly, riding on its many-veined and transparent wings—wings that may vibrate as many as 1600 times a minute—can hover, shoot ahead, zoom upward, dive, and even fly backward. The American authority on the *Odonata*, Dr. James G. Needham, of Cornell University, once told me of seeing dragonflies outdistance swallows. Many species can travel for considerable distances at express-train speed.

There are times when dragonflies, glinting in the sun, seem, in truth, what Tennyson called them: "Living flashes of light." Only a few species are abroad late in the dusk and some species are so responsive to the sun that they invariably alight when even the slightest cloud obscures its rays. One western species of dragonfly never takes to the wing until the mercury rises to 100 degrees F. Above a mill-pond on any hot, still, midsummer day, the dragonflies are always especially active.

The larger of these hunters often have regular beats; they hawk back and forth over the same stretch of pond-side or stream-bank, week after week. Invaders are driven off with a wild clatter of chitinous wings. Sometimes, two dragonflies will hover menacingly, head to head, rising high into the air. A small dragonfly, in Indiana, once maintained authority over a single tall rush stem. It permitted other dragonflies to come into the vicinity but not to settle on this particular private perch. On certain sections of the Wabash River, dragonflies of some species have followed exactly the same courses over the same areas generation after generation.

In following such beats, the insects are on the alert for food. They harvest it on the wing. Occasionally they may sweep some insect alighting on a leaf into their jaws, but in the main their food consists of insects caught in full flight. If you watch a dragonfly, you see it shoot toward some hovering insect, rush on full tilt, and leave behind it an empty space where an insect was. Sometimes the mosquito hawk catches its victims in its jaws but more often they are scooped from the air by means of its legs.

The legs of a dragonfly deserve special attention. They are bunched far forward, so far, in fact, that they are of little use in walking. The dragonfly is one of the most completely aerial of living creatures. One of the chief uses of its six spiny legs is to form a kind of butterfly net, an aerial seine in which to capture its victims. Flying at full-tilt, it scoops its prey out of the air. Then, with its forelegs, it transfers the captured insect to its mouth.

Out of this spine-and-leg-formed basket it takes such food as horseflies, bees, small moths, butterflies and even such a large catch as a luna moth. The American entomologist, William Beutenmüller, fed forty horseflies to a captured dragonfly in the space of two hours and the insect's appetite was far from satisfied. Dr. Leland O. Howard discovered that a dragonfly is capable of eating its own weight in food in half an hour; and it still will be ready for more. Probably no other inhabitant of the insect world, with the single exception of the praying mantis, has such a voracious appetite for living food.

The wings of a dragonfly are amply large to support almost any prey that comes to its bunched legs. When one scientist cut the wings of a dragonfly, bisecting them longitudinally, as was explained before, he found the insect could fly virtually as well with wings of only half the supporting area. William T. Davis, for many years honorary president of the New York Entomological Society, once captured a curiously deformed dragonfly in the Half-Hollow Hills region of Long Island. It had two wings on one side of its body and one on the other. Yet, in spite of the fact that there was twice as much supporting surface on one side of its body as on the other, it flew as swiftly and maneuvered as expertly as did the normal dragonflies. Of all insects, none is more adept at dodging a collecting net than the dragonfly. Some species are so wild and shy that entomologists have had to shoot them on the wing, using very fine powder-shot to bring them down.

The motor muscles which operate a dragonfly's wings comprise approximately one-quarter of its weight. These powerful muscles enable the insects not only to fly at high speeds but to travel for surprising distances. In the South Seas, one species of dragonfly has colonized an island which lies 200 miles away across open water from its original home.

The most widespread distance-flights of dragonflies occur during the great migration years. In the United States many of the larger dragonflies make long migratory movements southward in the fall. When unusually heavy rains in the spring flood lowlands and enable dragonfly nymphs to escape from fish into shallow water, a larger number of the insects reach their adult stage and swell the movement toward the south. Along the great rivers of the European continent, such spectacular mass migrations have also been noticed. As early as 1494, the flight of millions of these dragonflies down the valleys of the Rhine and other rivers attracted wide attention and was noted in early manuscripts. In 1839, spectacular dragonfly flights of the kind occurred all over Europe.

W. H. Hudson, both in *Far Away and Long Ago* and in *A Hind in Richmond Park*, recalls the swift migration of storm-pursued dragonflies across the pampas of Argentina which he witnessed as a boy. The insects appeared flying before the *pampero*, a violent summer wind from the southwest. "From a minute or two to as much as fifteen or twenty minutes before the wind struck," Hudson recalled, "the dragonflies would appear flying at their utmost speed. They always appeared to be in a panic, and if the wind was close behind, on coming to a grove or plantation they would rush into it for shelter and there remain, and on the following morning they would be seen hanging from the trees, clinging together in masses, like swarms of bees, and the masses would sometimes cover entire trees as with a brown and crystal drapery."

Occasionally, the migration of dragonflies carries them far out to sea. One hundred and seventy-five miles off the coast of Africa, passengers on a liner observed the members of one such group winging their way to certain death. In the dune-country of northern

Indiana, at the lower tip of Lake Michigan, I have seen green darner dragonflies come in from over the water obviously exhausted by long-sustained flying. They tumbled onto the sand, barely able to make the beach. But they were safe after long wandering over the vast plain of water.

Some years ago, when a two-day storm from the northwest had carried great numbers of dragonflies out over Lake Michigan from the Wisconsin shores, the wind suddenly shifted to the east and the waves washed the drowned insects up on the beach. Following the driftwood line, one entomologist counted an average of nearly fifty dragonflies for every three feet of his advance.

Storms and winds thus take their toll of the dragonflies. So do other enemies of the adult insects. Kingbirds snap them up and swifts and swallows scoop the smaller species from the air. One foreign bird, the bee-eater, *Merops perscicus*, is said to capture dragonflies for the sole purpose of stripping off their wings and using them for lining its nest. Bats sometimes capture twilight dragonflies and the webs of the orb-spiders snare others. Insectivorous sundew plants have been known to engulf and digest the bodies of small dragonflies which alighted on them. Speeding automobiles break the bodies of dragonflies against their radiators. Frogs, fish, and watersnakes dine on dragonflies whenever the opportunity offers. The heads of thirty-five dragonflies were once removed from the stomach of a single two-pound trout.

Against all its foes, the insect has its speed of wing and its keenness of vision. The dragonfly has one of the world's finest pairs of compound eyes. It can see in virtually all directions at the same time. It is also far-sighted. Make a sudden movement thirty feet away and one species of dragonfly will dart sidewise in a swift evasive dash. Some of these insects can see small objects, like other dragonflies, at least 100 feet away.

If you examine the huge bulging eyes of a dragonfly, with their thousands and often tens of thousands of massed six-sided lenses, you will frequently observe them glowing with what seems to be a tinted internal light. Sometimes the hue is green or blue, some-

THE MAY FLY lives so short a time it never eats. It is the only insect that molts again after it has reached its full size and has attained its wings.

RESEMBLING living twigs, the walking stick insects are well camouflaged as they move slowly about feeding on the foliage of bushes and trees.

SOMETIMES called the mosquito hawk, the dragonfly feeds voraciously. It catches smaller insects in flight and devours them while on the wing.

TERMITES exchanging food, upper left. Right, a male field cricket among beanpods. Below, two female crickets with slender egg-placers projecting behind.

times it is red or gray or brown. This tinted glow is the reflection of light from the interior of the eye.

Although the dragonfly, by virtue of its wide destruction of mosquitoes and other insect pests, is one of man's best friends among the six-legged, it is almost universally disliked and is the villain in many superstitious beliefs. It is supposed to doctor and feed snakes. It is supposed to sew up the ears of children. It is supposed to sting horses. It is known as the Devil's Darning Needle. A few of its other designations, such as The Water Maiden and The Demoiselle, reflect the beauty of its form and movement.

Appropriately enough, one of the earliest of the airplanes, the light bamboo-and-silk machine designed by the pioneer aeronaut, Alberto Santos-Dumont, the Brazilian who, in France, made the world's first public airplane flight, was named *The Demoiselle*. In the air, the dragonflies exhibit some of their most brilliant feats of flying at mating time. Some species perform a kind of courtship dance and the duels between rival males bring out spectacular exhibitions of airmanship.

'After mating, the females deposit the innumerable eggs which hatch into the muddy-hued, underwater children of the dragonflies. Some species scatter their eggs along the surface of the water; others drop them in more or less compact masses. Still others creep down plant stems and place the eggs in slits in the tissues, remaining beneath the surface sometimes for half an hour or more. From a single female dragonfly, Dr. Leland O. Howard once obtained 110,000 eggs. In spite of the enemies which attack and devour the eggs, vast numbers hatch each year.

One of the strangest of the enemies of the dragonfly egg is the so-called "fairy fly." This minute hymenopterous parasite descends beneath the water, swimming with its wings, to seek out and lay its own eggs on the eggs of the dragonflies. Instead of dragonfly nymphs, other fairy flies appear from the parasitized eggs. Almost microscopic in size, the little parasites carry down their own supply of air when they make their amazing journey into what, for them, must be great depths of water.

After the eggs of the dragonflies have been deposited, life for these insects goes on the same as before. They skim the water and the vegetation along the banks of ponds and streams, gleaning their food from the air. As autumn advances, the larger dragonflies such as the green darner, *Anax junius*, fly farther and farther afield. On windy October days you find them coursing over high weedlots and in the lee of woodlands.

Food gradually becomes scarcer as the weeks pass. Chill, late-autumn downpours find the dragonflies clinging to the underside of leaves, motionless and numb. The autumn rains are succeeded, in northern states, by autumn frosts. Later and later in the morning the dragonflies cling, chilled and stupefied, to the streamside vegetation. Only during the hottest hours of the day are they active on the wing. Life for them is running down. Then comes the night of the first freeze. Among the rime-covered flags and cattails and other lowland plants, morning finds their lifeless bodies. Their generation has passed. But, always, another is maturing unseen among underwater weeds of pond and stream.

3. THE LIFE OF
THE TERMITE

IN A SOUTHERN state, a few years ago, a real estate man was inspecting a large hotel that had been vacant for some months. He started to step out on the ballroom floor when something peculiar about the finish caught his eye. He investigated. Only a paper-thin shell of floor remained. Termites had excavated away almost all the boards, leaving only a thin film of wood at the top and bottom.

A housewife in New York City leaned her elbow on a kitchen table at breakfast. The table collapsed under her. Termites, eating their way up from the wood of the floor into the wood of the table, had riddled the legs with their tunneling.

In South Carolina, a school opened after the summer vacation. The librarian took down a book. It was honeycombed with small burrows. She took down another and another. In hardly more than three months' time, the whole school library had been destroyed

85

by termites.

Each year the tiny jaws of these wood-consuming and paper-eating insects produce more property damage in the United States than lightning, tornadoes, and arson combined. In 1960, the figure was placed at $250,000,000. It had more than doubled in twenty years. With North America's climate growing milder and with the construction of more houses employing central heating, termites have extended their range northward. In 1938, a survey of 100 homes in Indianapolis, Indiana, showed only three contained termites. Ten years later, forty of the 100 dwellings were infested. The species that cause the greatest damage in the United States all belong to the same genus, *Reticulotermes*. Termites are now found in every state in the Union except Alaska. In Europe, as well as in North America, these insects have been on the move. In France, within recent years, they have spread northward from Bordeaux to Paris.

Wherever they live, they consume wood and woody material. They attack everything from factory buildings and piled lumber to airplanes and gunstocks and baseball bats. Although they sometimes kill living trees in the citrus orchards of California and Florida, termites live mainly on dead wood. They may dine on timbers more than a century old. Cellulose is their main food. Yet termites, by themselves, are unable to digest this food they live on. Within their digestive tracts they normally carry colonies of microscopic, one-celled protozoans. In one of the strangest partnerships in nature, these tiny organisms break down the cellulose into a form of nourishment the insects can assimilate.

In the economy of man termites are a greater menace than they are in the economy of nature. Most species are found in the tropics. There they riddle fallen trees, hasten decay and play an important part in clearing the jungle floor of debris that otherwise would soon make it impassable. In some parts of Africa, termites provide a highly favored food. After being roasted over a slow fire they are described as delicately flavored and nourishing.

For at least 50,000,000 years, termites have been consuming wood on the North American continent. In the State of Washington and in the Florissant beds of Colorado, fossil termites have been discovered in Miocene shale. An even older fossil, embedded in Eocene rock, has been unearthed in western Tennessee. It belongs to a genus represented today by a single species living in northern Australia. In all the world there are more than 1700 described species of termites. About fifty are known to North America.

At first glance a termite looks like an ant. It is commonly referred to as a white ant. Yet it is not an ant and, strictly speaking, it is not white. The termite is a primitive insect. It is most closely related to the cockroach. Thus structurally it is almost at the other end of the insect scale from the highly organized members of the *Hymenoptera* order to which the true ants belong.

If you look at a termite closely you will see that, unlike the thin-waisted ant, it is thick-bodied. In their workings in wood, termites leave no telltale sawdust as do the carpenter ants. In the case of the ants, the material is merely excavated to make tunnels. In the case of the termites, it is swallowed and, with the aid of their protozoan helpers, digested.

But, like ants, termites do live in large colonies. And within those colonies there are different castes, the workers, the soldiers, the reproductive members of the insect societies. The colony begins with the dispersal flight of winged males and females from a large and well-established nest. They issue forth like a rising cloud of smoke. For this once in their lives they are attracted to the light instead of being repelled by it. For this once they appear in the outer air. The sole purpose of their flight is to spread the species and establish new colonies. Most often this dispersal of the insects takes place in spring or early summer in clear weather after a rain has softened the ground. On their slender gauzy wings, moved by rather weak flight muscles, the termites navigate the air for only short distances. The direction of their flight is determined by the breeze.

Thousands of the insects are snapped up by birds, by lizards, by dragonflies. Those that survive break off their wings on landing.

87

Each of the four supporting surfaces has a line of weakness running along the base. Sometimes one or more wings will break off in the air and the insect will come spiraling down like a maple key. Termites never mate in the air as honeybees do. In fact, it may be weeks after they have landed, broken off their wings and paired, before mating takes place. But the founders of the colony, the termite king and queen, mate for life.

The first thing this pair of now-wingless termites does is seek out a crevice in the ground or in wood. Entering it they laboriously hollow out a small cavity. Only when this humble royal chamber has been completed and sealed in does the initial mating occur. In our northern species, the colony is slow in getting started. The queen, in some instances, produces no more than a dozen young the first year. These are always workers and soldiers. Usually they reach maturity sooner and are smaller than later members of the colony.

In contrast to the meager egg production of these northern insects, tropical termite queens are the world's champion egg-layers. They often produce from 8000 to 10,000 a day. Certain Australian queens are believed to lay as many as 3,000,000 eggs a year and to live, in extreme cases, as long as half a century. The body of the queen swells enormously with the production of this constant stream of eggs. Among African queens she sometimes becomes as large as a good-sized potato, 160 times the size of her mate, 2400 times the size of a worker. Her legs are no longer able to support the weight of her body and she is unable to stand. The tunnels are too small for her and she remains a prisoner within her chambers. Entombed for life, she may become the mother of 100,000,000 before she dies.

Each egg is licked and cleaned and cared for constantly by the workers and nymphs. Otherwise it would fall prey to mold. As the embryo slowly develops the egg absorbs water and its size increases, sometimes to as much as three times its original bulk. The tiny termite that hatches from the egg looks like an adult in miniature. Unlike the ants which hatch as helpless grubs, the

88

termites are never entirely dependent. They can move about on their six slender legs from the beginning. But they are slow in developing. Three months or half a year—or, in some cases, more than a year—go by before the nymph becomes an adult. A large part of the population of a typical termite nest consists of such soft-bodied, almost white, sightless immature insects. Molting half a dozen times, they grow larger. But they have no pupal period, undergo no major transformation. At any stage in their development they can be recognized as termites.

At first they receive drops of liquid food from workers of the colony. From such food, passed from mouth to mouth, they obtain the one-celled protozoans that help them digest the wood they later swallow. As each skin is shed at molting time, the envelope is chewed up and consumed as food. A termite nest is extremely clean. Workers continually lick and clean the nymphs. In return, the older termites obtain food in the form of exuded materials. This curious interchange of food, it has been suggested, may have been the original impetus leading to the establishment by these primitive insects of their large and populous colonies.

Such colonies may vary from a few hundred individuals in our northern states to several million in the nests of tropical species. Dr. Alfred E. Emerson, in his studies of South American termites, found one nest that contained at least 3,000,000 insects. In central Africa, some nests are believed to have even greater populations. One reason for the size of such termite colonies is the relatively long life of the insects. Workers may live three years, or even longer, as compared to the six-week summertime span of a worker honeybee.

Each termite home, whether in the tropical jungle or in the basement of a city dwelling, requires two things: darkness and dampness. The greatest living enemy of the termite is the ant. It was to escape the attack of ants that these wood-consuming insects adopted their hidden way of life. Besides ants, numerous other creatures prey upon them, especially at times of the dispersal flights. Fifty-two species of birds eat North American termites. As many as 1100 termites have been found in the stomach of one flicker. In South America, the so-called anteater consumes more termites than ants. With its long claws, it rips open the nests and then runs its slender tongue in among the galleries to extract the soft-bodied insects. None of these enemies, however, presents so great a danger as the threat of drying out.

Because most termites have soft bodies, devoid of a hard outer shell, they rapidly lose their moisture when subjected to dry air. They shrivel and die. To avoid this, they live in darkness, like insects in a cave. When they cross masonry foundations in traveling from their subterranean nests to the wood of a dwelling, they construct tube passageways that spread like exposed, branching roots across the open concrete or rock. In this manner they remain hidden and avoid exposure to the drying effects of the open air. Only the winged males and females that emerge on dispersal flights enter this dangerous realm. They are darker in hue, harder of body, less sensitive to dryness.

Although termites succumb quickly in dry air, they can survive in emergencies that would prove fatal to many other larger and stronger creatures. In 1951, a warehouse in Kansas City, Missouri, was discovered to be infested with termites. Pest control men were ready to start eradication measures when the city was visited by one of the worst floods in its history. For seven days, the lower part of the warehouse, containing the termites, was submerged. That week under water, it was assumed, had eliminated the destructive insects. One good deed was chalked up for the flood. Then the waters receded, the mud was shoveled out, and an examination showed that all the termites were alive and hungry, chewing away on the building with renewed appetites.

Not infrequently a number of years, often half a dozen, go by before the presence of termites is discovered in a building. The workings of these insects leave no telltale sawdust such as is found around wood infested by carpenter ants. The galleries of the termites are plastered smooth with the brownish, mortarlike residue of wood from which the nourishment has been extracted. Usually it is the presence of the branching passageways extending upward to the wooden framework of a building or—more frequently—the emergence of the winged males and females at dispersal time that leads to the discovery of the wood-eaters. Apparently an extremely delicate sense of smell leads the termites to wood. In the tropics they have been found tunneling horizontally underground for 100 feet or more and then turning directly upward when they arrived under a log. In another instance, during a single night, they constructed a covered passageway to the top of an iron table and began feeding on a small wooden box that had been placed upon it.

Within each termite colony there are several castes. The winged and sexually mature males and females that issue forth on the colonizing or dispersal flights form the First Reproductive Caste. There is also a Second Reproductive Caste capable of producing eggs in an emergency. The males of this group are sexually mature although they never develop wings and retain the forms of nymphs. If anything happens to either the original king or queen, replacements are forthcoming from the Second Reproductive Caste. The substitute queens produce fewer eggs, so several are required to carry on the work of the primary queen.

In the Worker Caste there are also males and females. But they are sexually undeveloped and are unable to produce eggs. Wingless and usually blind, they devote themselves to the chores of the colony. They tunnel through wood. They digest the cellulose with the aid of their internal helpers. They feed the king and queen and other members of the colony that are unable to feed themselves. Nymphs and workers comprise the bulk of the population of a termite nest.

It is among the fourth group, the Soldier Caste, that some of the most unusual of these insects appear. With soft, vulnerable bodies in the rear, the soldiers possess huge armored heads and mandibles. In some instances, their heads are squared off so they can be used as plugs to seal the entrances of the narrow tunnels in the event of an attack. The soldiers click their jaws or knock their heads against wood to produce a rallying call that brings assistance to

91

whatever part of the nest is threatened with invasion. Termites are deaf but they are extremely sensitive to vibrations. It has been noticed that railroad ties, jarred by passing trains, are almost never invaded by the insects. Neither, as a general rule, is the woodwork of factories containing heavy vibrating machinery.

In some species, a different type of soldier is especially effective. These insects are known as the nasuti, "the nosed ones." Their heads are drawn out into a pointed snout with a small hole at the end. From this opening a thick fluid is ejected in sticky threads. Invading ants are soon gummed up with this insect glue and rendered helpless. The fluid is also employed in cementing together fragments of earth and wood to form the passageways and above-ground nests of certain species.

None of the termites living in the United States builds exposed nests that rise above the ground. But in the tropics, particularly in Africa and northern Australia, termites live above the ground in what are, considering the size of the builders, skyscraper apartment houses. Honeycombed with interconnecting passageways, some of these nests are as much as twenty-five feet high. Players at one unusual golf course in central Africa tee off from the flat top of a termite nest fifteen feet in the air. On this course, the hazards are formed by nearly 100 other nests, each almost as big as a cottage.

The walls of these nests, formed of saliva-cemented particles of soil and wood, are often so hard it requires a pickaxe to break through. One entomologist reported that sparks flew when he attacked a nest with a hatchet. In leveling an area of such termite nests, when the land is intended for cultivation, large and powerful bulldozers are required. Yet the teeming insects build such mounds in a surprisingly short time. It has been reported that termite nests large enough to endanger landing aircraft have risen on tropical airfields almost overnight. Some of the huge nests have rainshields that function like eaves. Others are peppered with tiny holes, like pores, for ventilation. When the material of the nests is crushed up and rolled into place it is said to produce tennis courts that have a permanently smooth and resilient quality.

92

Of all the nests of the termites, probably the most interesting are found in the vicinity of Darwin, in northern Australia. They are the homes of the famed compass termites. About twelve feet high and ten feet long and three feet or so thick, they are oriented in a north and south direction. The sides face east and west in almost every instance. Like huge headstones in some graveyard of giants, they extend across wide stretches of open land. This arrangement of the nests, with the greatest expanse offered to the morning and afternoon sun, is believed to provide a means of temperature control for the galleries within.

Such varied facets of termite life are endlessly surprising. But the most remarkable single thing about these primitive creatures is the fact that, in spite of their forming one of the lowest orders of the insect realm, they have succeeded in developing a social life and a caste system that resemble those of the most highly organized of all the insects—the ants, the wasps, and the bees.

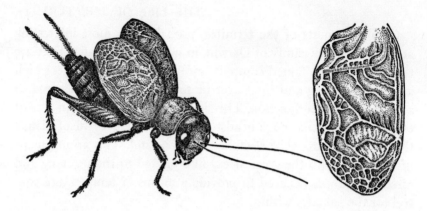

4. THE LIFE OF
THE CRICKET

ORTHOPTERA

THE CHIRP OF the black field cricket is known to almost every state in the Union. From coast to coast, and from the Canadian line south to the Rio Grande, its nightly serenades are a familiar feature of the late-summer darkness. In northern states, in autumn, the polished black bodies of these crickets leap and weave among the grass stems or dart in little explosions from beneath any board that is lifted from the ground. Cricket life reaches its annual climax in the days before the autumn frosts begin.

It is during these days that the females are busy depositing the minute eggs which form the starting point for a new generation of crickets which will, in turn, fill the nights of another summer with the sound of their fiddling. In southern states many of the crickets overwinter as immature insects or remain active the year around as adults.

By jabbing into the soil her needle-like ovipositor—an egg-placer

94

which often is as long as the rest of her body—the female field cricket deposits as many as 300 tiny, banana-shaped eggs. Each egg is about one-twelfth of an inch in length. When laid, it is creamy white or straw-colored. The eggs are left in the ground singly or in bunches but they never are enclosed, as are the eggs of the locust, in a secretion-pod.

Throughout the winter they remain in the ground which alternately freezes and thaws, is bare and covered with snow. A period of dormancy and cold is needed for their proper hatching. Dig up cricket eggs before the first freeze and bring them into a heated house for the winter and you reduce their chances of hatching. Instead of protecting them, you are really harming them. Like numerous seeds which need a period of cold to sprout properly, the eggs of the cricket are benefitted by their winter's stay in the frozen ground.

It is usually late May or early June before the eggs are hatched by the rays of the sun warming the soil in which they are buried. The baby crickets are devoid of either wings or ovipositors. They crawl out of the soil and into the sunlight above the spot where, the autumn before, the female had deposited her eggs. From the beginning, these field crickets are, like their parents, omnivorous. Their jaws will bite into dead insects or nibble plant tissues as the opportunity offers.

From day to day they grow until their swelling bodies can no longer be contained within the chitin shell of their original skeletons. The skin along their backs splits and they crawl out in new attire. They have made the first of their many molts. Before they reach their adult forms, they may have as many as a dozen different skeletons, each larger than the one before. The winged cricket appears in the final molt.

The body of the adult field cricket is between three-fifths inch and one inch in length. Its antennae are half again as long as its body and, at the other end of the insect, the spiked cerci—which project to the rear like two pointed tail-feathers—are about a third the length of the body. These twin spines are present in both the

95

males and the females. They have a special function. Tiny hairs on them catch delicate vibrations, either on the ground or in the air. These vibration-detectors are, to a certain extent, auxiliary hearing organs for the crickets. Their main hearing organs are represented by small elongated openings just below the knees on the insect's front legs.

Because of the glistening black of these insects, it is difficult to see the features of a cricket's face. Hanging down beside its powerful jaws, however, are easily observed palpi. These finger-like organs aid the insect in eating and in locating food that is close at hand.

A field cricket has lived from nine to fourteen weeks when it sheds its skeleton for the final time and attains its adult form. The many-veined wings, which appear then, differ according to the sex. The wings of the males alone possess the special file-and-scraper feature which provides them with the fiddles they use in their music-making. A heavy vein at the front of each wing has a roughened, file-like surface on the underside. On the upper side of these wings there is a scraper. By moving his wings the little musician rubs the file and the scraper across each other much in the manner of a bow and a fiddle.

The wings are usually elevated at an angle of about forty-five degrees when the cricket is making its music. Each shrill chirp is projected for a surprising distance by the tightly stretched membrane of the wings which acts like a sounding board. In reality, the familiar chirp of a cricket is a rather complex sound. Dr. Frank E. Lutz, of the American Museum of Natural History, used sound-track recordings to study it. He found that the single chirp that we hear is actually made up of three beautifully executed "slurs" such as an expert violinist might produce. Each of these component sounds lasts slightly more than a fiftieth of a second. The first two are followed by split-second silences of even shorter duration. Our ears, of course, cannot catch the tiny pauses and the three sounds merge into a single shrill chirp which has a duration of about one-tenth of a second. In its fundamental notes, the chirp of a cricket is in the octave just beyond piano range.

96

The rate at which one of these ebony musicians repeats his chirps depends largely upon the position of the mercury. On cool autumn evenings the fiddling of the crickets becomes painfully slow. While not as delicately attuned to the temperature as the snowy tree cricket, the dusky field musicians increase or decrease the tempo of their music with the rise and fall of the thermometer.

The quality of a cricket's music often varies according to the emotions of the musician. In the presence of a rival, his sound rises and takes on a sharper and more challenging note. When the male is wooing a nearby female, the chirping is more melodious; at times, it has an almost tremulous sound. In the main, the music of the crickets is for the ears of the females alone. These twilight solos are serenades. Male crickets, deprived of their music-producing wings in one laboratory experiment, attracted no mates. From a distance of thirty feet or more, female crickets have been seen heading for a chirping male, obviously attracted by his serenade.

These serenades attract other males as well as the females. On numerous occasions I have seen second males approach and challenge the singers. This challenge is not for a musical competition. It is for a battle as fierce as a fight between wolves. Falling upon each other, two fighting crickets will bite and kick, claw and twist. I have seen one cricket tear away a leg and another an antenna. Sometimes when the battle ends it has brought death to one of the contestants. More often, however, the defeated cricket limps hastily away, escaping with his life. The conqueror, elevating his wings and moving them rapidly from side to side like a triumphant rooster crowing in a moment of victory, sends forth his shrill, chirping song.

In his engaging book about the insects of his suburban lot, *A Lot of Insects*, Dr. Lutz notes that just as people fold their hands, some with the thumb of one hand uppermost and others with the thumb of the other hand uppermost, so some crickets have the right wing and others the left wing on top. It appears to make no difference in the music. During the first hour or so after the final molt, while the wings were still comparatively soft, he could reverse the lapping

97

order. Once the wings have hardened, however, the insect maintains the same arrangement throughout life. If the hardened wings of a cricket are placed in a position that reverses the natural overlapping, the insect seems uncomfortable. It wiggles about until it gets the wings back in the same position they were before.

Although a cricket rarely flies, it often sails through the air in remarkably long standing broad-jumps. Anyone who has tried catching a cricket can attest to its liveliness. The hind legs of these insects are equipped not only with powerful muscles but with sharp spines that dig into the ground like the spiked shoes of a sprinter. Other spines on its legs point backward. They are believed to aid the insect in scrambling about among the grassblades by giving it a firmer grip on the leaves and stems as it leaps and runs and climbs.

A cricket's front legs have a special use at mealtime—which for many crickets seems to be all the time that is not spent in musical pursuits. While its powerful jaws are at work, the insect often holds its food with its forelegs. No squirrel gripping a nut hangs on more tenaciously than does a black field cricket, once it has come upon something edible. And its ideas of what is edible cover a multitude of substances. It nibbles away at everything from old shoes to juicy lettuce, from grass-seeds to rubber, from meat to alfalfa. In the satisfaction of their eccentric appetites, crickets often cause considerable damage. They devour grain in the shock and tomatoes and beans on the vines. Many a farmer has left a jacket or a pair of gloves or a hat in the field and later discovered that it had provided many crickets with a meal. The insects are attracted particularly to clothing that is stained with perspiration or food.

When not eating or singing, the field cricket is often found sitting in the doorway of its private home, a little cave hollowed out beneath some stone or clod of dirt. This doorway is located, whenever possible, where the rays of the sun will fall directly upon it. Sitting there in the warmth of the afternoon sun, the cricket makes its toilet. The antennae are always its special concern. These many-jointed feelers are run through the insect jaws, washed and dusted with the greatest care. To clean a wing of every speck of dust the cricket swings it far forward. It scrapes its abdomen along the ground. It puts its foot in its mouth and bites off particles of dirt. It twists and contorts itself, minute after minute, until the toilet is complete. The curious and often ludicrous poses that a field cricket assumes during this cleaning-up process are superbly illustrated in a series of sketches made from life which appear in *The Grasshopper Book* by Wilfrid Bronson.

Because the actions of crickets can be observed so easily, they make excellent pets. A glass fruit jar, or an old-fashioned lamp chimney pushed an inch or so down into sand in a flowerpot and covered with mosquito netting, makes a satisfactory cage. A watch crystal or other shallow container will provide a watering trough while a few grains of oatmeal, some fragments of lettuce or melon, a chicken bone or bit of meat, will supply all the food required. If meat is not included in the diet, pet crickets seek it by resorting to cannibalism.

One woman in the eastern United States, who kept crickets in an apartment near a large cathedral, discovered a direct relationship between the chiming of the church bells and the music of her insects. Just as playing a phonograph will start canaries singing, so the sound of the bells stimulated the crickets into musical activity. As soon as the church bells began their pealing, the insects began fiddling away in their cages.

Out in the open fields, the life span of a cricket living under normal conditions carries it from early summer to the time of heavy frosts. While crickets are comparatively hardy, they almost all die when the thermometer drops to the point where their tissues freeze. Only rarely do they live until spring. A field cricket generation, in northern states, has completed the cycle of its life weeks before winter arrives in earnest.

Long before that time, also, the female crickets that have been wooed with music have employed their slender ovipositors to plant in soft moist earth the eggs upon which the continuation of the

99

species depends. From these overwintering eggs will come children they will never see—children of another generation and another year.

In the United States, the black field cricket is probably the commonest and most widespread member of the *Orthoptera* order. But it is only one of a vast group numbering more than 1000 species in North America and 22,500 in the world. Relatives of the crickets, all belonging to this same order, include such varied creatures as the walking sticks that appear to be twigs broken off and come to life; praying mantises that wait for their victims with spiked forelegs upraised as though in supplication; and katydids with green, leaflike wings and music that speaks our language. There are the cockroaches of evil odor and reputation, but of ancient lineage and amazing life habits. There are the innumerable grasshoppers—the coneheads that appear to be wearing dunce's caps; the green meadow grasshoppers that fill the night with their high, steely buzzing; the locusts, or short-horned grasshoppers, that show their brilliantly colored hind wings as they hover with a fluttering crackle in the hot summer sunshine. There are the many crickets—the burrowing, secretive mole cricket; the straw-colored house cricket, *Gryllus domesticus*, hero of Charles Dickens' *Cricket on the Hearth*; the pale green tree crickets, one of which, the snowy tree cricket, is the only insect instrumentalist that joins with its fellows and plays in unison as in an orchestra. Then there is the so-called cave cricket or camel cricket, pale brown and secretive, living under stones and old boards and in cellars, an insect that looks like a cricket, acts like a cricket, but is, in truth, not a true cricket at all but rather a wingless, long-horned grasshopper.

So diverse are the members of the huge *Orthoptera* order that another insect from the same group will be treated in the next biography. Its activities and abilities and surroundings are far different from those of the black field cricket. It is that creature of striking appearance and curious habits, the praying mantis.

100

5. THE LIFE OF
THE PRAYING MANTIS

ORTHOPTERA

IT MAKES NO sound; it is voiceless. It turns its pointed, inquisitive face this way and that; it is the only insect that can turn its head like a man. It merges with the foliage of its background; its body is camouflaged in greens and browns. It remains for long periods in a pious attitude with forearms uplifted as though in supplication; it is thus that it awaits the approach of its victims. This creature of curious attributes is the praying mantis. Sometimes it is known as The Soothsayer, the Nun, or The Devil's Rearhorse.

Almost as long as your hand, the winged adult insects seem to make their appearance suddenly late in summer. Many people think they have come as a flock of migrants. In truth, they have been there all the time. So well camouflaged is the mantis, so silent are its ways, that it is rarely noticed until it reaches its full size, develops wings, and begins to fly about. The males, slenderer and more active than the females, sometimes rise high in the air and cover considerable distances. Nearly 100 of these insects, in a single week, landed on the observation tower of the world's tallest structure, the Empire State Building in New York City.

In the United States there are four species of praying mantises. One is native; the others have arrived accidentally as immigrants. The native mantis is *Stagmomantis carolina.* It is found throughout the South and as far west as California. *Mantis religiosa,* the European mantis, reached our shores from France about the time of the Spanish-American War. It probably came in the form of an egg-case attached to packing material used to protect nursery stock and made its first appearance in a nursery near Rochester, New York. At almost the same time another immigrant insect, the Oriental mantis, *Tenodera sinensis,* appeared on shrubs in another nursery near Philadelphia, Pennsylvania. It had come from the other side of the world, from China. A fourth species, *Tenodera angustipennis,* also appeared, later on, in the Philadelphia region. This Oriental mantis has narrower wings than *T. sinensis* and produces an egg-case of an entirely different form.

From the nurseries where these immigrants first arrived, they have spread out over a wide area. The European mantis has worked its way west and north across the Canadian line and now is established in southern Ontario. The original Oriental mantis, *T. sinensis,* is common through New Jersey and southern New York, and has found its way to Ohio and other states beyond the Alleghenies. The second Oriental species, *T. angustipennis,* is also increasing its range. By 1944 it had reached Long Island. In the spring of that year I found the first *T. angustipennis* egg-cases reported from the area attached to wild cherry twigs near Baldwin, Long Island. All of the praying mantises, because of their endless appetites for insect prey, are special friends of gardeners and farmers. They are virtually the only insects introduced accidentally into America that have proved beneficial to agriculture.

A mantis will attack anything within reach that moves. Its main diet consists of a succession of beetles, bugs, caterpillars, and other insect prey. But it will catch a hornet or a bumblebee just as readily as it will a squash bug or a housefly. I have found a mantis with a captured swallowtail butterfly and another with a large green darner dragonfly. There are records of these predatory insects capturing humming birds, Cecropia moths, mice, and DeKay garter snakes. I once watched an immature mantis, hardly two inches long, attack a full-grown tomato worm twenty times its bulk. Although it was unable to hold its prey, it put it to flight. A mantis seems afraid of nothing. It will rear up and box with a kitten or it will hold its own with a pugnacious English sparrow. While it is fearless and combative, ever on the alert for insect prey, it is entirely harmless to man.

Each autumn, when the full-grown insects begin to appear in the region of New York City, such institutions as the Bronx Zoo and the American Museum of Natural History receive a flood of inquiries. They come in by telephone and by mail. The inquirers want to know what the strange insect with the spiked forelegs is and whether it is dangerous or not. Few other insects attract as much attention.

In Times Square, a mantis reared up on a fire-plug always is surrounded by a crowd of curious spectators. In a Middle Western city, a few years ago, traffic stopped on a main street while the motorists watched a pitched battle between a sparrow and a mantis. The sparrow, incidentally, was the one that first gave ground. In the house, a mantis makes a docile pet. It will eat proffered insects, and even bits of corned beef or hamburgers, and will remain in one position on a plant for hours at a time. A few years ago, a leading magazine ran an article on "the mantis cult," pointing out the number of people who had tried their hands at keeping such insect pets. In at least one large biological laboratory, the praying mantis is substituting for the guinea pig as the subject in various tests.

The story and life habits of all the species of these insects is much the same. That of the commonest mantis of the eastern United States, *Tenodera sinensis*, begins in the warmth of the late spring. All winter long the rounded egg-case, about the size of an English walnut, has remained attached to some twig or weed-stem. This marvelously wrought mass of hardened froth was produced by the female of a previous generation and attached, the autumn before, to its present support. In a central compartment, enclosed within a tough wall, are the elongated eggs. From 125 to 350 of them are ranged together like cordwood within each egg-case.

The hazards of the winter are numerous. Sometimes mice gnaw into the egg-cases and reach the central compartment. Sometimes woodpeckers drive their chisel-bills into them and consume the eggs inside. Sometimes grassfires consume the weeds to which the cases are attached. But in spite of these hazards most of the egg-cases survive until spring. As the warmer days lengthen, the balls of hardened froth become softer and more spongy. Then one morning, usually between eight and ten o'clock, hatching begins.

Down the front of each egg-case is a narrow strip of overlapping plates. It suggests a vertical row of tiles placed one above the other. The hatching insects wriggle out between these plates. Each is honey yellow and is enclosed in a membranous sac. Dangling head downward from a silken thread, which extends from the rear of the sac into the interior of the egg-case, the baby insect pushes and struggles from time to time. Around it are scores and sometimes hundreds of other young mantises dangling in exactly the same manner.

It is at this time that the praying mantis passes through one of its most dangerous periods. The newly hatched insects are soft, defenseless, vulnerable to attack. Ants sometimes swarm over the mass of dangling mantises, carrying off the living booty in large mouthfuls. Throughout its later life, the praying mantis avoids the tiny ant. While it will attack a wasp or hornet with complete disregard for its sting, it does not strike at a passing ant. I have never known a mantis to take an ant when it was proffered as food. The antipathy between these insects is evidently lifelong.

In its struggles, the dangling baby mantis works itself free from the membranous sac. Its threadlike antennae begin to move about; its hairlike legs carry it upward over the mass of its brothers and sisters and it comes to rest on the top of the egg-case or clinging to the twig that supports it. Here its chitin shell hardens and darkens. A quarter of an hour later, its honey yellow has changed to light brown. It is ready for its life as a hunter of living prey.

Each mantis is a lone wolf. It searches for its own food and exists by virtue of its own skill. Should one of its kind come within reach of its spiked forelegs, it would snap at it as quickly as at any other prey. When an egg-case hatches within a closed cage, the number of young insects rapidly decreases through cannibalism.

Probably the first food of these hunting insects are plant lice and similar six-legged minutiae. As the mantises grow larger by successive molts, they take on larger and larger prey. I have seen a half-grown mantis ambitiously stalking a black swallowtail butterfly and another, hardly larger, struggling with a moth in its grasp. One mantis captured and ate most of the body of a deadly black widow spider.

In every instance the insect captures its prey in the same manner. With its folded forelegs lifted in a reverent attitude, it remains motionless among the leaves—or moves cautiously forward like a stalking cat—until its victim is within reach. Then out dart the forelegs. The two parts, with the spikes facing each other, clamp shut over the back of the prey. The victim is unable to move, imprisoned as though in a toothed steel trap.

Always, the mantis begins to devour its prize in the same way and at the same spot. No matter whether it has caught a wasp, a butterfly, or a grasshopper, it begins by biting into the back of the insect's neck. This quickly severs the main nerve ganglia. Once when I came upon a praying mantis with a shrew gripped in its forelegs, I found it biting into the fur on the back of the animal's neck. The shrew may have been dropped by a cat or it may have been captured by the mantis. At any rate, its body was still warm. And the interesting thing is that the mantis was attacking this huge and abnormal victim just as it attacked a fly or a bee, biting its way into exactly the same part of its anatomy.

Nothing seems to affect the digestive systems of these insect predators. They have eaten green paint, daubed on insects for pur-

105

poses of identification. They have devoured insects which have been taken directly from ammonia, from cyanide killing jars, from wood alcohol. I have seen a mantis munching away contentedly on the spiny hairs of a caterpillar. Swallowing food, any kind of food, seems to be the mantis' chief source of enjoyment.

By the time one of these insects has eaten its way through June, July, and August, in the region of New York City, it is ready for its final molt. At that time, its slender, gauzy wings appear and it is full-grown. In the air, it flies on its four fluttering wings with its neck outstretched in the manner of a wild goose. Favorite hunting spots of these insects are butterfly bushes, goldenrod clusters, and wild cherry trees—especially when they form bushy clumps a few feet high.

Indian Summer finds the life of the adult mantis in its concluding weeks. It is in the autumn that mating, and that strange cannibal feast which often follows it, takes place. The female devours her husband, sometimes in the midst of the actual mating. In fact, one female may devour more than one male. Fabre cites an instance in which a female mantis consumed eight of her suitors. The males seem strangely unconcerned over their fate. They are more active; they can fly faster and farther and higher; they can easily escape. Instead, they hardly put up any struggle. They seem mildly interested spectators at the banquet rather than its *piece de resistance*.

The female begins by clamping her forelegs over the back of the male. Caught in this vise, he is powerless to move. Methodically, the female then sets to work, biting through the insect-armor which protects the back of his neck. Even after the male is headless, he can raise his wings, walk, and even attempt to fly. It is an eerie sight to observe a decapitated insect lift its wings as though in battle or reach out with a leg and catch a branch as it is falling through the air and then pull itself up on this support. The nerve centers of the mantis are located in various parts of its body; the unaffected ones go on functioning even after the brain is gone.

Following her bizarre wedding feast, the female mantis produces one or more froth-cases packed with eggs. The work of producing

106

such a case occupies the better part of two hours. The female always hangs head-downward. She never glances at the object she is creating. This whole marvelous activity is a sequence of actions dictated by instinct.

White, pastelike material, beaten into a froth, appears from the tip of her tail. At first, it is carefully worked around the twig or weed-stem to provide a firm foundation. Then the tip of the tail begins moving slowly, methodically in a gradually expanding circle. It is building up the mass of froth much in the manner of a threshing machine producing a strawstack. The operation continues with hardly a pause. When most of the froth is in position and has been formed into the desired shape, the movements alter. The tail pauses. It moves to the center of the foam-mass, buries itself there, and for a time changes its position but little. A pumping motion produces rhythmical pulsations along the insect's abdomen. The eggs are being placed within the ball of froth.

For a long time this delicate work continues. Then the tip of the tail begins its slow revolutions again, building up the bottom of the case. Finally, all is completed. The case glistens in the sun. The froth is sticky and resembles the beaten white of an egg. Without a backward glance, the female walks away in search of insect prey to appease her hunger.

As days go by, the white of the egg-case darkens to yellow, then to brown. It becomes tough and the wall of the inner compartment, within which the eggs are housed, takes on a leathery hardness. In midwinter, a safety-razor blade will hardly cut through this inner wall. Within this rounded house marvelously wrought from a mass of almost formless froth, the eggs are protected from the winter weather and from many of the enemies which might destroy them.

To the attacks of one curious little enemy, which preys on some species of mantises, *T. sinensis* appears to be immune. This parasite hides beneath the base of the wing of a female mantis. There it remains patiently, day after day. It is awaiting the hour for which it was born. This hour comes when the making of the mantis' egg-case is in progress. The parasite creeps backward along the larger insect's abdomen until it comes to the very tip of its tail. Here it clings and when the pumping motion begins, sending the mantis eggs into the interior of the froth-mass, the little insect goes into action. On the passing eggs, it deposits its own almost invisible ones. Within the case, they will hatch and its children will feed on the larger eggs and will be protected by the very case that is being produced to shelter the eggs of the mantis.

With the end of the mating season, and the completion of the egg-cases, the climax of life is over for the praying mantis. In northern states, it is a creature of a single summer. The end of warm weather is the end of its adult life. Even when a mantis is brought indoors and fed on plump crickets and other insect fare, even when it is kept warmed day and night, it lives only a few days—or weeks at most—beyond the span of its normal existence.

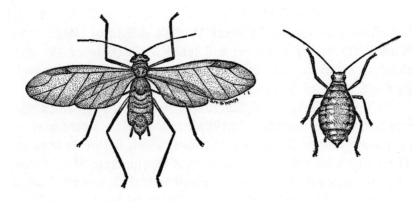

6. THE LIFE OF
THE APHID

HOMOPTERA

NO FARTHER away than the nearest garden you can meet a creature that illustrates to the full the bewildering strangeness of insect ways. This is the familiar plant louse, or green fly, the aphid of rosebush and plant-leaf.

Massed shoulder to shoulder, their sharp sucking spears sunk in the plant tissues, the aphides remain with hardly a movement for hours on end during the early summer days. They spend their time in the twin activities of drinking sap and bearing living young. Every aphid in the crowd is a female. Every baby that is born is also a female. Without mating, generation after generation, these virgin females begin, within a few days after their birth, to bear other females in their turn. It is this fantastic fertility of the aphides which saves them from extinction. They are frail creatures beset by many enemies. Yet, in spite of incessant slaughter, the race has spread and multiplied.

Anyone who has read Gilbert White's delightful classic, *The Natural History of Selborne*, will recall his account of the vast clouds of aphides which descended suddenly on that English parish on the first day of August, in the year 1785.

"About three o'clock in the afternoon of that day, which was very hot," White records, "the people in this village were surprised by a shower of aphides, or smother-flies, which fell in these parts. Those that were walking in the street at this juncture found themselves covered with these insects, which settled also on the hedges and gardens, blackening all the vegetation where they alighted. My annuals were discolored with them, and the stalks of a bed of onions were quite coated over for six days after. These armies were then, no doubt, in a state of emigration, and shifting their quarters; and might have come, as far as we know, from the great hop plantations of Kent or Sussex, the wind being all that day in the easterly quarter. They were observed at the same time in great clouds about Farnham, and all along the vale from Farnham to Alton."

Similar clouds of wind-borne aphides have been seen at other times and in other parts of England. The poet, James Thomson, refers to a myriad insects "engendered by the hazy north." A belief of his day was that these clouds of insects were produced by a wind from the North or East. The explanation for their dramatic appearance from these quarters is undoubtedly the one mentioned by White: They most frequently came from the great hop-growing centers of Kent and Sussex.

In 1943, New York papers ran special boxes on two invasions of aphides. On the last day of July, a breeze from the East brought untold millions of the insects from Long Island over lower Manhattan. Window-screens were almost solidly coated; the tops of parked cars seemed covered with moss; pedestrians walked with newspapers protecting their heads. Again, in early September, countless aphides appeared over the Bronx section of the city. They hung, according to the newspaper account, "like a sweeping canopy over the Grand Concourse from Burnside Avenue to 180th Street."

110

Pedestrians were soon covered with alighting aphides. Shop windows, automobile windshields, screen doors, and the windows of elevated trains became plastered with the insects. All taking part in this great mass movement were members of a winged generation. Such a generation appears occasionally and under curious circumstances which will be related later in this chapter.

How many of the tiny plant lice comprised the living clouds that descended on Selborne and New York no one can tell. Counting them would be hardly easier than determining the number of water-droplets in a giant thunderhead. But entomologists, over a period of several centuries, have employed time, paper, and pencils to calculate the staggering hypothetical populations which the rapidly multiplying plant lice might produce. These minute insects, rarely more than one-quarter of an inch in length, represent fertility reaching an awe-inspiring peak.

A few years ago, two American entomologists, W. P. Flint and C. L. Metcalf, noticed that the underside of the leaves of a tulip tree were covered from one-tenth to nine-tenths with masses of green-and-rose-colored aphides. At random, they picked 100 leaves and counted the number of plant lice on each. The average came to 340. At a conservative estimate, they decided, there were 100,000 leaves on the tulip tree. All appeared as badly infested as the 100 leaves that were picked. This meant that the leaves of that one tree were supplying food for a population of more than 30,000,000 aphides!

Two hundred years before Flint and Metcalf, the French scientist, Reaumur, spent hours sitting at his desk and covering sheets of paper with figures in an effort to discover how many descendants a single aphid might have by the end of a summer season if all lived and reproduced. The answer he arrived at was 5,904,900,000. Toying with this idea, he placed—in his imagination—his tenth-of-an-inch insects in military formation, four abreast, and discovered that the procession would extend for 27,950 miles. It could circle the equator and have hundreds of miles of marching aphides left over.

Other biologists have dramatized the fertility of the plant lice in different ways. The great Thomas Huxley pointed out that the descendants of one aphid, at the end of summer, theoretically would form so great a bulk that they would equal the weight of all the inhabitants of China. Recently, a scientist reported that a single hop-aphid, breeding unmolested for a year, would have six sextillion tenth-of-an-inch progeny—enough to form a head-to-tail line extending so far into space that it would take a ray of light, starting at the outer end, 2,500 years to reach the earth!

These fantastic possibilities, of course, are never realized. A host of predators and parasites keep the plant lice continually in check. To many insects, the massed forms of the aphides are living pastures on which they feed. Ladybird beetles, both in their immature and mature forms, devour them. The child of the lacewing fly wreaks such havoc among their massed forms that it bears the common name of "aphis-lion." One of the flower flies, *Syrphus americanus*, lays its eggs among the aphides and the hatching larvae feed on the plant lice. So do the carnivorous caterpillars of the wanderer butterfly. They specialize on woolly aphides among the alders of ditches and streamsides.

Birds eat plant lice; praying mantises begin their predatory careers by attacking them; daddy-longlegs are said to feed upon them at night. One of their most terrible foes is a tiny chalcid fly, a waspish parasite which deposits, through an ovipositor as sharp as a hypodermic needle, eggs in the backs of feeding aphides. Each egg is a seed of death. It hatches into a ravenous larva which consumes its host and then pupates within its hollow skin. Emerging from its pupa-case as an adult, it cuts a hole, as round as though made by a can-opener, in the back of the aphid's skin and flies away. Sometimes, you will see a score of the dry brown skins of the dead aphides, each with a round hole in the back, clustered close together on a plant stem.

Other factors, besides the constant foraging of insect enemies, keep the aphides from running amuck. Cold rains in the early spring deplete their ranks and fungous and bacterial diseases take their toll. There is an ebb and flow in the fortunes of the tiny plant lice. A few years ago, pea-aphides increased abnormally in the Willamette Valley of the Northwest. As a consequence of extremely favorable weather conditions, they multiplied so swiftly they threatened destruction of the whole pea crop. However, the same weather conditions furthered the development of a fungus. It spread rapidly through the aphid multitudes, wiping out fully 95 per cent of the insects, and bringing their population back to normal again. Nature maintains her balance in many and devious ways.

How important it is for us that Nature's checks keep the fertility of the plant louse within bounds is illustrated by the spectacular spread of the grape aphid, *Phylloxera vastatrix*, through the vineyards of France. This aphid reached Europe about the time of the American Civil War. In the United States it lived largely on wild grapevines and did little damage. But its accidental introduction into France placed it under new conditions. It flourished and multiplied tremendously. Like a devastating fire, it swept through the great vineyards of southern France, laying waste a total of 2,500,000 acres, approximately one-third of all the cultivated grapes of the country. This one insect, hardly more than one-twenty-fifth of an inch in length, cost France a greater sum than all the indemnity she had to pay at the close of the Franco-Prussian War.

By 1885, the grape aphid had spread to Switzerland, Russia, Turkey, Spain, Germany, and Algeria. It had even found its way to Australia. Although a prize of 300,000 francs was offered in France for an effective means of combating the ravages of the insect, no method of control succeeded until the European grapes were grafted on roots brought from America. These roots had been associated with *Phylloxera vastatrix* for centuries and had developed an immunity to the attacks of the aphid.

Such examples of aphides running wild are few. Their enemies see to that. Against their many foes, the plant lice have a single, curious mode of discomforting the enemy. Literally, they gum up the attack. Pointing upward like twin cannon, two short tubes project from the rear of the insect's abdomen. When a foe approaches from the rear, yellowish drops of wax, which are exuded from these tubes, are sometimes pushed back into the face of the attacker. By the time this rapid-drying insect-gum is cleaned from its face, its intended victim has had time to move away to a new position. A special mechanism within the body of the plant louse permits wax-laden blood cells to escape into the stubby tubes from which the masses of wax are expelled.

This odd form of defense is, of course, feeble at best. The most effective form of protection the aphides know is obtained by a sort of bribery. In effect, the plant lice hire a guard of mercenary soldiers to watch over them while they feed in peace. Warlike ants act as sentries, driving away insect predators, and in return they obtain the sweet honeydew given off by the aphides. All species of ants seem inordinately fond of honeydew. It has been called "the national dish of the ants."

This sweet fluid is a by-product of digestion. Its composition varies in the same aphid when the insect is sucking sap from different plants. Usually, it contains some 85 per cent of carbohydrate and 3 per cent of protein. The honeydew is given off in drops, a single sap-sucking insect exuding as many as forty-eight drops in one day. By stroking the backs of the aphides, the ants induce them to give off additional honeydew. Sometimes an aphid will be milked of honeydew drops by several ants in succession. Since the days of Carl Linnaeus, plant lice have been known as the milk cows of the ants. This curious partnership has been in existence for millions of years; ants and aphides have been found embedded together in Baltic amber. To the very end of summer, the ants watch over their herds of insect cows. Throughout the last of October, and even into early November, I have seen them in attendance during sunny hours obtaining the last of the sweet fluid.

For many generations, this honeydew was one of the unsolved riddles of natural history. Pioneer scientists wrinkled their brows over its origin. An early English translation of the writings of the Roman naturalist, Pliny the Elder, reflects the attitude of his day.

114

A BLACK swallowtail butterfly imprisoned in the spiked forelegs of a praying mantis. At rest, the mantis lifts its forelegs in an attitude of prayer.

DURING summer, aphides reproduce without mating. In autumn, winged males and females appear, producing fertile eggs that carry the species over winter.

GAUZY-WINGED and golden-eyed, the lacewing fly feeds on aphides. In its larval form it destroys so many plant lice it is called the aphis-lion.

THE HOUSEFLY is an efficient germ distributor. It may travel for a dozen miles and carry on its body as many as 6,000,000 disease bacteria.

"It (honeydew) is either a certain sweat of the skie, or some unctious gellie proceeding from the starres, or rather a liquid purged from the aire when it purifyeth itself." Pliny made three guesses. And all were wrong.

Even in the eighteenth century, in Gilbert White's day, the source of honeydew still remained unknown. Writing on the fourth of June 1783, White observes: "Fast honey dews this week. The reason for these seem to be that in hot days the effluvia of flowers are drawn up by a brisk evaporation, and then in the night fall down with the dews with which they are entangled. This clammy substance is very grateful to bees, who gather it with great assiduity, but is injurious to the trees on which it happens to fall by stopping the pores of the leaves. The greatest quantity falls in still close weather because winds disperse it and copious dews dilute it and prevent its ill effects. It falls mostly in hazy warm weather."

The fact that honeydew does damage the leaves of trees sometimes works to the aphides' own disadvantage. Sooty fungus develops in the coated leaves, damaging the tree and thus reducing the food supply of the insects.

On the backs of some species of aphides, a mass of fluffy white wool-like wax provides a special form of protection. Contact sprays kill the usual aphid, but not one of these woolly aphides. Still other species, including the injurious cherry-aphid, curl leaves over and remain protected within them. This leaf-curling is a purely mechanical process. It results from draining the fluids away from the central section of the underside of the leaf. Protection of another kind is afforded by the making of galls, or swellings on plants, within which certain aphides live out of sight. Because the dampness within these galls might further the development of deadly fungi, the aphides give off a white powder which counteracts the effects of the dampness.

The life story of most aphides follows the same general pattern. It begins with the laying of the egg in autumn. At that time, winged males and females appear and mate. The egg is cemented in some protected location such as in the crevices of bark or at the base of a winter bud. Millions of these eggs are destroyed during the months of winter. Chickadees feed on vast numbers while winter rains and thaws and sleets tear many of the others from their moorings.

But when spring arrives, there are always many left to supply the "stem mothers" for the colonies of another year. The eggs are timed to hatch just when tender foliage is right for piercing with little sucking spears. Inside these sharp little proboscis-beaks there are four piercing needles. The aphid inserts its proboscis in the plant tissues, forcing it farther and farther until it reaches vital food stores including sugar. The plant fluids are drawn up the tube of the proboscis and digested within the body of the plant louse. Honeydew and wax are discarded as waste-products.

The sun rises only a few times before the rapidly growing aphid, always a female, is ready to give birth to the first of a long line of living young. It was in 1762 that the French scientist, Bonnet, made the startling discovery that all summer generations of aphides are produced by virgin birth. In some species, such as the hop-aphid, *Phorodon humuli*, a female begins producing young when it is only three days old. These plant lice give birth to as many as seven children a day. Where there are 200 hop-aphides one day, conceivably there may be 1000 the next.

The temperature, of course, affects the reproduction of the aphides, lengthening or shortening the number of days between generations. When the weather is chilly, with the thermometer standing at around sixty degrees F., a new generation appears once in two weeks. But, in hot weather, when the mercury has risen to eighty degrees, that time is cut nearly in half. During a relatively short summer season, more than a dozen generations of plant lice may follow each other in rapid succession.

In *Science* for January 27, 1893, Prof. M. V. Slingerland, of Cornell University, published the results of a remarkable series of experiments with aphides. For two years and ten months, he had raised plant lice under carefully controlled conditions. Isolated females were watched and, as soon as they produced young, these baby plant lice were isolated. Thus contact with other aphides was

116

made impossible. For sixty-two generations, these insects produced nothing but females. Not a single male appeared. A European scientist, also keeping his insects under constant summer-temperature conditions, raised rose-aphides for four years without obtaining a male. In natural conditions, as we will see a little later, males normally make their appearance during the cooler weather and shortening days of autumn.

The first aphides to appear in summer soon become plump little bags of sap. They move about but little and cling for days in one position. Around them, the massed bodies of their children, and the children of the other stem mothers, increase steadily in number. Often they form an unbroken blanket of insects covering inch after inch of a rose-shoot or plant-stem. Tiny, newborn babies walk over the backs of the older insects searching for an open space where they, too, can insert their little sucking spears in the plant tissues and take up their stand amid the insect flocks.

The different species vary in color and in habits. There are cherry-red aphides, black aphides, aphides with patterns on their backs, aphides that appear in most of the shades of the rainbow. One species has the habit of taking positions in more or less definite rows on the stems of sunflowers. S. W. Frost discovered that when he touched one of these anchored little insects, he could produce a movement which would run like a wave up or down the stem. The movement of one insect caused the successive movements of all the others.

Day by day, the colony of aphides, springing from the original stem mothers on a plant, enlarges. In spite of the work of many enemies, the massed insects cover more and more of the stem or leaf on which they are located. Overpopulation and starvation seem to threaten. The fertility of the wingless plant lice seems about to overrun and defeat itself. What happens?

A generation of winged females appears. They sail away, riding the air currents on the frailest and most transparent of supporting surfaces, wings with surprisingly few strengthening veins, but wings that often carry them far. Alighting on other plants, they become the stem mothers of new colonies. Their children are wingless and again the swift multiplication of the plant lice goes on until the sap-sucking hosts produce still another generation with wings.

This successive appearance of winged females accomplishes many things. It spreads the species. It opens up new pastures for the comparatively sedentary aphides. It also leaves behind numerous enemies which become established at the site of an old colony. Often, by migrating to a different species of plant, the aphides make it still more difficult for their enemies to follow them. The hop-aphid, for example, normally lives for three generations on plum trees, eight on hop vines, then migrates back to its original food-source when autumn comes.

Why the winged females make their appearance at the time when they are needed most is still something of a mystery. Crowding may be one factor. The quality of the sap undoubtedly is another. In a California laboratory, one American scientist found that he could produce a winged generation at will simply by altering the chemical composition of the sap in plants on which the aphides were feeding. Many species of plant lice inject chemicals through their sucking beaks and when large numbers are feeding on the same plant this may be sufficient to alter the composition of the sap enough to cause the appearance of a winged generation. In other experiments, it was revealed that grape aphides produced winged forms as soon as they were fed on dry or wilted leaves. During the long sequence of generations observed during Prof. Slingerland's researches at Cornell, not a winged insect appeared. His plant lice were well fed, were kept under constant summer temperature conditions, and were not crowded.

When the shortening days of autumn arrive, another dramatic event occurs in the life of the aphid. The adult insects cannot survive through cold weather. Some means of carrying the species over to another spring is necessary. Again there appears a generation of a different kind. They consist of true males and females. They mate and the females deposit eggs. These sexually perfect aphides are usually smaller than the summer insects which produce

118

living young. The females are wingless; the males sometimes have wings, sometimes do not. So fleeting is the life of these autumn males that, like the May flies, they are born without mouths and never eat.

The eggs of the apple aphid, smooth, shining, black, and oval, are cemented near the buds on the fruit trees. With the coming of another spring, the hatching aphid will find close at hand the unfolding tissues of the tenderest and juiciest part of the tree. On willows, some plant lice deposit their eggs on the bark of the tree trunk. Then they cover them over with a whitish substance which blends with the gray of the bark and makes them harder to detect.

That the shortening days, reducing light and plant growth, is the controlling factor in the dramatic appearance of the male and female aphides has been proved by numerous experiments. In laboratories, where light and temperature could be controlled, scientists have played tricks with the inherited reactions of the little plant lice. By extending the hours of artificial lighting during the winter, they have kept them producing only living young. On the other hand, when spring came, they shortened the hours of lighting and —although it was entirely the wrong season by the calendar—the confused plant lice produced a generation of sexual males and females.

The story of the plant louse completes its cycle with the killing cold which in autumn slays the hosts of the adult outdoor aphides in a single swift catastrophe. That is the conclusion for virtually all these insects in northern states. But, for one species at least, the eggs that are left behind have a curious winter adventure of their own.

After the true females of this species, the corn-root aphid, *Aphis maidi-radicis*, have laid their eggs on vegetation, ants carefully pick them off and carry them into their underground nests where they watch over them throughout the winter months. As many as 1000 of these aphid eggs have been taken from a single anthill.

In the spring, the young aphides hatch out within the ant's underground chambers. Cornfields are not advanced sufficiently

119

for them to find nourishment on the roots of the corn plants. So the ants carry them carefully in their jaws, tunnel into the ground beside the roots of smartweed and deposit the aphides where they can obtain food while waiting for their normal host to develop. When the corn is well-established, the ants return and transport the honeydew-producing plant lice from smartweed to cornstalk-root. Here they visit them constantly, milking them for honeydew in their new pastures.

When fall comes again, and the aphid eggs are laid, the ants once more collect them and carry them underground. The cycle of this remarkable relationship between ant and aphid begins anew. In this relationship, the operation of an insect dairy reaches its most complex and efficient form.

All members of the *Homoptera* order, numbering more than 30,-000 species throughout the world, fold their wings like a peaked roof. This characteristic distinguishes them from the *Hemiptera* which fold their wings flat above their bodies. Both orders possess sharp-pointed beaks for sucking. The cicada is the largest member of the *Homoptera* order. Its shrill song in the treetops is familiar on hot summer days. The celebrated seventeen-year cicada burrows underground as a nymph for more than a decade and a half before it emerges as a winged adult. Other close relatives of the aphid are the scale insects, the lantern flies, the mealy bugs, and the leaf hoppers. The tree hoppers, tiny creatures able to leap for surprising distances as well as fly, appear in such grotesque forms that they are popularly known as brownie bugs. Another familiar insect belonging to the same order is the frog hopper. It is less often noticed than the mass of shining white bubbles with which, in its immature form, it surrounds itself on plant stems and leaves. Within this airy shelter it feeds protected from enemies and the desiccating rays of the sun.

7. THE LIFE OF
THE CHINCH BUG

HEMIPTERA

EVEN WHEN it has attained its full growth, a chinch bug's body will extend less than a third of the way across a copper one-cent piece. Yet the annual damage wrought by this black-and-white insect is estimated to be the equivalent of 5,000,000,000 of these coins. Together with its brothers and sisters, aunts, uncles, and cousins, the chinch bug drains away $50,000,000 worth of sap from American cornfields and grainfields each year.

No other member of that vast family of the true bugs, the beaked and flat-winged *Hemiptera*, does as much damage as it does. It attacks not only corn and wheat, but millet, oats, barley, rye, timothy and other grasses. The astronomical numbers of the tiny sap suckers multiply their individually small damage to gigantic proportions.

In one Illinois wheat field, two entomologists picked stalks at random and found there were an average of fifteen chinch bugs to

121

a stalk. In an acre of wheat there are about 1,000,000 plants. Thus the chinch bug population of a single acre of infested wheat may be greater than the combined human populations of New York and Chicago. And the insects may extend in the same proportionate numbers across a whole countryside. As early as 1909, the chinch bug had already cost American farmers a total of more than $350,-000,000.

This all-too-familiar insect of the Middle West was first described and named by Thomas Say, the Father of American Entomology who lived at New Harmony, Indiana. He called it *Blissus leucopterus*. All told, there are more than 1300 species of chinch bugs known to science and the insect is worldwide in its spread. Most of the species feed on wild grasses and do little damage. It is *Blissus leucopterus* that sweeps in a devastating tide across farmlands. It is this species which, at various times, has brought ruin to whole farming communities.

The first outbreak of the kind recorded in America occurred in the wheat fields in North Carolina in 1785. During several succeeding years, the insects were so numerous that farmers abandoned planting wheat. In 1809, a recurrence of the insect-scourge laid waste grainfields in the same area. By the time of the Mexican War, the chinch bug had traveled as far west as Illinois, Indiana, and Wisconsin. During the year 1850, the chinch-bug loss in Illinois was put at the equivalent of four dollars and seventy cents for every man, woman, and child living in the state. The Civil War year of 1864 saw the chinch bugs so destructive in this state that in its richest farming sections one-half of all the corn and three-fourths of all the wheat was lost. The wheat loss was estimated at 30,000,000 bushels; the corn loss at 138,000,000 bushels; and the total monetary loss at $73,000,000.

In computing insect losses, it is customary to estimate the number of bushels the agricultural pests destroy and to multiply that figure by the selling price of the produce that year. As Harry B. Weiss, for many years head of the bureau of entomology of the state of New Jersey, pointed out in the *Journal of the New York*

Entomological Society, an essential factor is ignored in such calculations. If the millions of bushels of grain which pests have destroyed were added to the total for the year, the price would automatically drop. By lessening the crop, the insects raise the price of each individual bushel. Using this price for calculating the monetary loss necessarily increases the resulting sum. Nevertheless, the annual loss from the chinch bug is undoubtedly very great. In pioneer days, families were on the verge of starvation as a result of the activity of this small insect invader.

So small, so silent, so unobtrusive is the reddish-yellow-legged, black-and-white chinch bug that in some regions farmers were unable to account for the sudden browning of their timothy or the sudden wilting of their corn. The fields seemed bewitched. Farmers were ruined without being able to determine the cause. The 1896 outbreak in Ohio was so severe that a government report states that nothing except fire ever caused such an enormous financial loss within the same period of time in an equal area.

These sporadic and immensely destructive outbreaks, when the insects seem to appear from nowhere as though part of some plague such as visited Pharaoh in the days of Moses, have their explanation in the weather. Abnormally dry years usually bring with them the hosts of the chinch bug. The insect's way of life is the key to its immense numbers and to those sudden spectacular flareups when it sweeps like a flame across the grainfields.

During winter months, the chinch bug hibernates as an adult. The insects squeeze into protected cracks in old logs, beneath loose shingles, under the bark of dead trees, in mullein rosettes. They secrete themselves in old haycocks and strawstacks, in the matted grass of fence-rows, in piles of woodland rubbish. They congregate in such numbers beneath half-buried fence-rails and old boards that are left lying on the ground that farmers often make a practice of lifting such coverings and destroying the insects beneath. But the favorite spot of all for the hibernating chinch bug is deep in the massed stems of a large grass clump.

In 1928, a Kansas entomologist made a winter census of scores

123

of bunch-grass tussocks. In a single clump, he found 529 chinch bugs bedded down for their long period of inactivity. Another investigator once picked approximately 1000 chinch bugs from a tuft of bunch-grass only three inches in diameter. Many of these overwintering bugs die before spring. Some are devoured by rodents, some are killed by cold.

Those that survive await the arrival of sunny days when the temperature remains for several hours at or above seventy degrees F. On such days, they open their wings, which have remained folded across their backs all winter long, and rise into the warm spring air. This initial flight usually ends in some wheatfield where the vivid green of young stalks is showing above the ground. Although the alighting insects immediately begin sucking sap, they do little damage. It is not their generation, but a later one, which the farmer needs fear.

In settling on the wheat, they are seeking only nourishment enough to fly about for a time, mate, and for the female to lay her eggs. After the eggs are laid, these adults sometimes fly on to a cornfield and settle in numbers on the young stalks. Alarmed at their sudden appearance, the owner of the field imagines the whole crop is endangered. In truth, this host of worn out adults lives but a short time and then disappears. The real threat lies in the generation hatching from the innumerable eggs left behind by the females.

These eggs are oval and amber-colored and about $\frac{1}{32}$ of an inch in length. The diameter of each egg is scarcely one-fifth its length. A female chinch bug will lay approximately 500 eggs, placing them behind the sheaths low on grasses and grains, in cracks in the ground, around the bases of plants, or directly on the roots of stalks of grain. The eggs are not laid all at once. Instead, they are deposited at the rate of twenty or so a day. It may take a female as long as a month to place all her eggs in position for hatching.

The interval between the laying and the hatching of the eggs varies widely according to the weather. It may be as short as seven days or as long as forty-five. When the tiny egg splits open at the

124

end, the minute bug which crawls forth is red with a wide white band across its middle. To see its markings you must view it under a magnifying glass, for the whole insect is so tiny it would take two to equal the size of a pinhead.

The eggs do best in a cool, moist, but not wet, locality. Heavy rainfalls during the early weeks of spring do much to check the multiplication of the chinch bugs. Driving rains during the hatching period beat the young bugs into the mud from which they are unable to extricate themselves. They also cover eggs with mud and prevent their hatching and keep the females from depositing a normal number of eggs. Again, wet weather stimulates the development of various kinds of fungi that attack and kill the insects. "Chinch-bug fungus" is a friend that comes to the aid of the grain-grower during wet seasons. Efforts to introduce such fungus artificially in infested fields have been made with some success by economic entomologists.

As soon as a baby chinch bug is born, it is able to run about on the tiniest and frailest of legs. It ascends a wheat-stalk and sinks its sucking-beak in the plant tissues, draining away draughts of sap. Adults and young are sometimes seen clustered together near the bottom of a stalk. Because of the difference in the time the first and the last eggs were laid, there are frequently bugs in many stages of development massed on the same plants. As the lower tissues grow tougher, the chinch bugs ascend higher and higher on the plant. In certain dry areas, where wind-blown sand drifts about the lower portions of the plant, the insects are found only on the extreme upper leaves where they are safe from the flying particles of quartz.

During each of the several molts which carry the immature bug to its adult state, the insect changes its form, its size, its coloring, and its pattern. Wings appear at the time of the final molt. Growing up for a chinch bug is a process that takes approximately twenty-eight days from hatching time.

Eventually the wheat stalk on which the clustered chinch bugs are busily engaged in draining away the sap becomes withered.

125

The insects migrate to another stalk, one that is still fresh and juicy. In this way, they rapidly spread across a field. In the latter part of June, when the grain begins to ripen and grow dry, there comes the most dramatic event in the life of the chinch bug. It is a mass-migration to another home.

In other fields, the cornstalks are shooting up higher and higher, day by day. To the chinch bugs, they are flowing rivers of sap. The insects begin a long and arduous journey, a trek on foot that continues for hours. Strangely enough, even the insects with wings walk with the rest; they make no effort to avoid the labor of the long migration. Singly and in straggling bands, the chinch-bug hosts plod ahead; they toil through the dust of country roads, clamber over clods in open fields, cross dry ditches, struggle through the tangled jungles of hedgerow grass, and finally, at the end of their epic march, reach the Promised Land of the cornfield.

These long treks usually begin on the afternoons of sunny days. When the weather is cloudy, the chinch bugs will continue streaming across the open ground during most of the hours of daylight. The migrants are in almost all stages of development; some are small and some are large, although most of the vast assemblage have yet to attain their wings. Sometimes the journey they make extends for a quarter of a mile or more, a vast distance for their tiny legs and one that is equivalent to a hundred thousand times their body length.

It is during this overland trek that the insects are most vulnerable to the control measures applied by the farmer. Once they gain the cornfields, they are almost impossible to eradicate. Preventing them from attaining the goal of their journey is the chief concern of the owner of the corn. By digging shallow ditches and preparing creosote barriers, by using calcium cyanide and by excavating posthole death-traps, he seeks to halt and destroy the invaders. How well he is able to succeed, at times, is shown by the fact that in a single week a half-mile barrier once stopped and destroyed 60,000,000 chinch bugs. Spraying and dusting have been tried in the war on these insects but the cost is often prohibitive. They

126

are used mainly to save small patches of valuable seed corn.

The migration which carries the chinch bugs from ripening wheat to growing corn is, in reality, only one of three migrations which the insects make. The first, as we have seen, consists only of overwintering adults and is from the winter quarters to the wheatfields. The second carries the maturing hosts from these fields to the fields of corn. The third, and final one, comes later on. When the corn begins to ripen, in its turn, the chinch bugs leave these fields and move to the grasses which provide late-autumn sap and a hibernating place for the winter. The number of bugs taking part in the first migration indicates the numbers that have survived the winter; those in the succeeding migrations indicate the numbers that have been born and have developed during the spring and summer.

The development of these latter chinch bugs comes to a climax in some retired place, beneath a leaf or under a clod of earth. The skin splits down its back for a final time and the last molt of its life occurs. Out crawls the adult bug, a dull pink creature with whitish wings. The pink flush soon fades and the insect assumes the black-and-white pattern it wears the rest of its life. Among the massed bodies of young and old chinch bugs on a plant, the pinkish forms of newly molted adults often stand out in contrast.

After the insects have become settled among the green cornstalks of a field, the eggs of a second generation are deposited by the females. This usually occurs in July. Throughout August, and on into September, the bugs, old and young, continue to find nourishment in the sap of the cornstalks. Eggs are still hatching in August.

It is during the months of August and September that the greatest damage to timothy is done by chinch bugs that have infested the hayfields. Oftentimes the insects which migrate to timothy instead of to corn begin operations at one side of a field and work across to the other side, leaving behind them dead grass as brown as though it had been swept by flames. The dividing line between luxuriant green timothy and the brown destroyed stems is sometimes no more than a yard in width. In the space of that

127

three feet, according to the government entomologist, F. W. Webster, there are the varying shades of green, yellow and brown, the shades representing the different stages from health to death. Sometimes the chinch bugs will be only part way across a timothy field when winter comes. The following spring they begin just where they left off and continue as before.

A number of farm crops are avoided by chinch bugs. Clover, alfalfa, vetch, soy beans, cow peas, peanuts, buckwheat, pumpkin vines, and truck crops are all safe from the inroads of the black-and-white sap-suckers. Only as a last resort, when all other sources of nourishment are gone, will one of these insects sink its beak into the tissues of such plants. It has been suggested that the rotation of crops, in which fields are planted on alternate years to clover or vetch, cow peas or buckwheat, be tried as a method of combating the injurious insects.

Combating the chinch bug, year in and year out, are a large number of its insect foes. The food of certain predaceous ground beetles at times is made up of 50 per cent chinch bugs. Because of its effective destruction of these bugs, one wasp-like parasite has been given the specific name of *benefica* by grateful scientists. This winged huntress, *Eumicrosoma benefica*, is so tiny it is rarely noticed. It deposits its minute eggs on those of the chinch bug. In certain localities, this beneficial parasite thus destroys from 35 to 50 per cent of all the chinch-bug eggs that are laid.

Birds of numerous species also wage war on the chinch bugs. Red-winged blackbirds, bobwhites, catbirds, brown thrashers, and meadowlarks consume immense numbers. In the stomach of a single brown thrasher, a scientist discovered more than 200 chinch bugs. In the stomach of a meadowlark, there were 100. Even house wrens have been observed feeding on the pests. Frogs sometimes eat chinch bugs and spiders ensnare the flying insects in their webs. But in spite of enemies, the tribe has prospered. And when the weather favors it, the agencies which ordinarily keep it in check are powerless to prevent this swiftly increasing multitude of the chinch bugs from overrunning the countryside.

128

The annual tide of the chinch bugs begins to ebb in the autumn. All those that overwintered the previous year have passed away and their children, the members of the first generation of the summer season, follow them, leaving only the young bugs of the second generation to carry over to another spring. Late in autumn, when the streams of sap in the cornstalks begin to disappear entirely, some of these chinch bugs have been seen eking out a meager livelihood by sucking juices from the silk on the ears of corn.

But by the first week in November feeding is a secondary matter. By that time, the remaining chinch bugs are seeking out tussocks of grass, and other protected spots, where they can hide for their months of hibernation. Winters with deep snows are best for the sleeping insects. Wet winters, with numerous thaws followed by sharp drops in the temperature, are disastrous ones for them.

However, even under the worst conditions, the small bugs are amazingly resistant to the effects of floods and freezings. When a winter flood swept across one Illinois lowland field, it washed corn out of the shocks and covered it with a sheet of ice. More than a week elapsed before the water subsided. Chinch bugs were discovered hiding in the ears. In spite of their long submergence, in spite of their encasement in ice, they crawled about, apparently unharmed, when they were warmed inside a farmhouse. Chinch bugs, observations have indicated, are able to survive through winters when the temperatures fall as low as twenty degrees below zero.

Thus the surviving adults reach the beginning of another summer. Their eggs provide the foundation for the vast hosts of these insects which, later in the season, reach such astronomical proportions. The might of the small—when the tiny is multiplied infinitely—is exemplified nowhere better than in the lives of such insects as the aphides and the destructive chinch bugs.

Approximately 23,000 species comprise the *Hemiptera* order. They include such varied insects as the water scorpions, the back

129

swimmers and the water striders, which skate across the surface film of ponds and streams in their hunt for food. There are squash bugs and stink bugs, bedbugs and thread-legged bugs and marsh-measurers and beautiful lace bugs. There are ambush bugs that lurk in the blooms of plants and await their insect prey and predacious assassin bugs, one of which bears the nickname of the masked bedbug hunter. There are the water boatmen that are able to produce sounds by rubbing their forelegs against their faces. There are the wheelbugs that seem to be carrying part of a cogwheel on their backs. Among the members of the *Hemiptera* order there are insects so tiny their characteristic forms and markings can be seen only with the aid of a magnifying glass. There are others as long as your forefinger. The giant water bug, known as the electric light bug because of its frequent appearance around street-lamps, attains a length of four inches in the tropics. It is the largest of all true bugs.

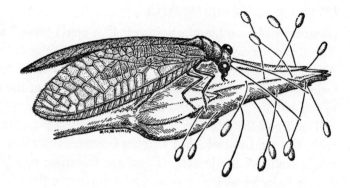

8. THE LIFE OF
THE LACEWING FLY

WHEN THE warm summer twilight falls, in almost any part of the United States, you can see frail, beautiful insects rise on filmy wings of the most delicate shade of green and flutter in the calm air. They are hardly more than half an inch in length. Compared to the direct and humming flight of a bee or the swift hawking of a dragonfly, their aerial excursions are slow and labored. They alight on plant leaves or weed stems, fold their four, many-veined wings into a wedge-shaped roof above their backs and, with long antennae pointing forward and great round, golden eyes staring to either side, they hurry forward on slender legs. They are seeking the aphides which form their living prey. These twilight creatures are those interesting and immensely beneficial insects, the lacewing flies.

Of course, they are no more flies than are fireflies, which are beetles—or ichneumon flies, which are related to the wasps. In

131

common parlance, too often, insects that aren't "bugs" are "flies." The former crawl and the latter fly. The lacewings belong to the *Neuroptera* order. Their near relatives are the ant-lion and the caddis-fly. They all have four gauzy wings instead of the two wings of the real flies, the members of the *Diptera* order.

The life of the lacewing is filled with surprising events. To begin with, the egg from which it hatches is unlike any other egg in the whole realm of the insects. If you are fortunate enough to see a female lacewing at laying time, you will observe the curious operation by which it is produced. This usually occurs in the calm of early evening.

The insect first touches the tip of her abdomen to the leaf or weed stem on which the egg is to be deposited. While it remains there a moment, a pool of glue-like secretion forms on the plant tissues. Then, in a quick movement, the lacewing lifts the tip of her tail. This draws up some of the viscid fluid into a long and slender thread-like stalk. The air quickly hardens it. At the top of this stalk, the oval egg is laid, standing upright on its stem. When first produced, it has a greenish tint; later, the green fades and the egg appears white.

As soon as this operation is completed, the female lacewing moves a few steps away and begins all over again. As many as 600 of these stalked eggs will be produced by a single female. They are deposited a few at a time. Like a row of miniature lollypops, they often extend down the sword-shaped leaf of an iris; at other times, they are clustered together on some rosebush infested with aphides.

The viscid fluid hardens into a tough, smooth support for the oval egg. Although it is thread-thin, hardly one-twelfth the diameter of the egg it supports, such a stalk can withstand great strains. Winds and storms lash them; rains drench them; the heat of midday pours down on them and they remain unaffected. For fully a week they have to support the eggs while the young lacewing larvae are maturing within them. So closely do these eggs resemble plant growths that some early naturalist classified them as the fruiting bodies of a kind of moss.

132

Sometimes, but rarely, ants pull themselves up the slender stalks and devour the eggs at the top. But it is less against such enemies than against the hatching lacewing larvae themselves that the mother insect places her eggs in as inaccessible a position as possible. The lizard-shaped little cannibals that hatch from these eggs are so voracious that, were the eggs of their brothers and sisters not placed beyond their reach, they would devour them all. In instances where the stalked eggs are placed close together, like bunches of lollypops, the first hatched of the larvae sometimes waits until the other eggs hatch, consuming each new larva as it appears. Even when they are well-grown and are many days out of the egg, these eternally hungry creatures will try to eat each other whenever they come face to face.

When it is ready to hatch, each larva cuts its way out of the egg with its jaws, circling and then pushing aside the top of the shell. It scrambles out over the rim, its dark, minute, lizard-like body supported by six slender legs. Shaped like calipers, its grooved sucking jaws project from its head. With these it pierces the sides of a victim's body and drains away the vital fluids within. The lacewing larva never chews its food; it takes only liquid nourishment.

Perched on the empty shell of the egg from which it has appeared, at the top of a high and slender stalk, the hungry lacewing larva first of all has to solve the problem of how to get down to the leaf or stem below. It accomplishes this apparently by attaching its tail to the smooth support as an aid to its descent. Once down, it hurries about, its head held low, its body decorated with a number of stiff, curved hairs which afford it some protection. Although they belong to different species, and even to different orders, the lacewing larva and the larva of the ladybird beetle look almost exactly alike, except for coloring. The dark little insect-lizard that is the immature lacewing is intent mainly upon one thing. This is the discovery of aphides.

Fortunately for it, the mother insect usually places her eggs on plants where aphides can be found. However, I have seen the minute larvae running over the bark of an apple tree for days.

133

One small twig of that tree held a patch of woolly aphides, hardly four inches long. The chances of the larvae finding their way among the ridges and crevices of the tree-trunk bark to the right limb and thence to the right twig, seemed remote indeed. Yet, feeding on those woolly aphides, there were eventually a number of the larvae. How many missed the mark no one knows. But the fact that a few succeeded was sufficient for the ends of Nature.

As a general rule, the chances are far more favorable for the larvae. They do not have far to go before they are among the thickly clustered bodies of the feeding aphides. These masses of aphides provide lush pastures for the hungry children of the lacewing. After their seven days in the egg, they begin twelve days of feasting. It is through this endless consumption of plant lice that the larva gains the name by which it is most widely known, the name of aphis-lion.

When they are not in action, the jaws of the aphis-lion appear to be four in number. But when they are in use, they fit together to form a single pair of curved and pointed piercing jaws. Approaching a soft-bodied plant louse, the squat larva opens wide the calipers of these jaws and then closes them, impaling its victim. Lifting its prey into the air, it lets the vital juices of its body trickle down through the grooves in the curved jaws. To obtain the last drop of this liquid fare, it twists about from side to side. Then it tosses the empty body of its victim, like a collapsed balloon or an empty sack, to one side and moves on to the next aphid. The whole process of impaling and draining a victim usually takes no more than a minute.

By the time it is nearing its full larval size, an aphis-lion is often destroying plant lice at the rate of almost sixty an hour. On some summer afternoon, when you have nothing else to do, try feeding aphides to one of these voracious creatures. One entomologist who tried that reports that the aphis-lion drained away the blood of so many victims he lost count. Yet, at the end of the performance, it seemed just as ravenous as it had at the beginning.

134

These bloodthirsty midgets will attack insects far larger than themselves which come within range of their jaws. They are fearless hunters. But their craving is only for cold-blooded animals. They are harmless to man. In fact, they are one of man's best friends among the insects. Their insatiable appetites for plant lice and more plant lice do much to keep the immensely fertile aphides from getting out of bounds.

One species of aphis-lion, a species found on pines and other conifers, camouflages itself and approaches unnoticed among the flocks of its victims. It is a wolf in the clothing of many sheep. It piles the skins of a number of its victims on its back. This small mound of deflated bodies moves when it moves and conceals it from all but especially watchful eyes.

During its larval life, the young lacewing grows rapidly. It molts at least twice. Its rate of growth depends largely upon the extent of its food supply. When an aphis-lion descends the stalk of its egg to a rose shoot which is one solid mass of aphides, it has a better chance for rapid growth than when it arrives on a plant where small and isolated colonies of plant lice must be hunted out, each in turn. The richer the pasture, the faster the rate of growth. At any rate, with the passing of from ten to a dozen days, the hurried feasting of the larva comes to an end. A time of great and sudden change has arrived.

Moving to the underside of a leaf, the larva attaches itself and draws its body up into a ball. Slowly it creates a white coverlet of silk, the cocoon within which it transforms into the winged adult insect. When new and shining, this cocoon suggests a pearl. It is spherical and about the size of a pea.

Days pass—sometimes as few as ten, sometimes as many as sixteen. Winds flutter the leaf and storms may beat upon it. Although it is well hidden from most eyes, this little ball of silk is sometimes discovered by one of the many wasp-like parasites. Inserting her ovipositor, she deposits her own egg inside. The larva which hatches quickly from it devours the transforming lace-

135

wing. This attack of the winged parasite is the greatest hazard the lacewing encounters during this period of silent and hidden change.

Near the end of this period, the transforming aphis-lion develops special cutting jaws which are used like can-openers to slice around the top of the cocoon and so provide a doorway of escape. One small section of the silken envelope is left uncut. It forms the hinge of the door. When the dome-like lid is pushed out by the emerging adult, it remains attached to the empty cocoon, tipped to one side and held in place by the silken hinge.

The insect, which crawls like a slow-motion Jack-in-the-box from the opening, finds some solid support and hangs vertically while its wings are pushed open by the pressure of the blood that is pumped into them. Gravity aids in the expansion of these many-veined supporting surfaces. While its wings and body harden in the air, the insect hangs motionless. As it clings there, shining and unblemished, its delicate Nile-green body and its great golden eyes make it a striking and memorable creature. It is well nick-named "the golden-eyed fly." These organs of sight shine with a metallic glint. They look like burnished gold in certain lights. At other times, they seem to glow with a phosphorescent shine.

Contrasting with its delicate beauty is the incongruous fact that the lacewing is an insect polecat. As a protection against ene-mies, it gives off a nauseating fluid. If any of this malodorous liquid gets upon your gloves or fingers it remains for hours. Scrubbing with soap and water, over and over again, only reduces its intensity. Time alone seems able to eradicate it. It is a strong, penetrating, disagreeable odor unlike any other that I know.

The life of this golden-eyed, green-bodied insect is a relatively placid one. It consists of resting among vegetation during the hottest and brightest part of the day and coming forth during the calm and beauty of sunset hours for the activities of feeding, mating, and egg-laying. How late the insects are abroad, I do not know. I have seen them active at midnight, fluttering in the beam of a flash-light. I have seen them at dawn, sipping from dewdrops and feeding

136

on plump aphides. While the appetite of the adult lacewing is not as insatiable as that of her aphis-lion offspring, she does valiant work in destroying additional plant lice. Sometimes, female lacewings have been known to become hungry during the process of depositing their stalked eggs and to appease that hunger by making a meal of one of the eggs they have just laid.

Brilliant, glaring lights attract lacewing flies just as they do beetles and moths. Some years ago, electric traps were installed in many eastern gardens and on lawns to kill pestiferous mosquitoes. Unfortunately the deadly traps were just as attractive to the lacewing flies as to the smaller pests. With these friends of the gardener being electrocuted wholesale, it was not surprising that the same gardens soon were overrun by aphides. The owners were killing their allies and aiding their enemies.

The coming of autumn cold reveals another surprising fact about the lacewing fly. In spite of its frail appearance, it is able to stand temperatures that paralyze or kill most other species of insects. A lacewing can take to the air at 36 degrees F. This is only four degrees above freezing. It can still walk about when the thermometer stands at 20 degrees—a full twelve degrees below freezing. This ability enables some lacewings to hibernate as adults in crannies and corners of country cellars. Sometimes they squeeze deep into the cracks in bark. In such cases, they almost invariably remain on the lower fifteen feet of the tree trunk. In cellars, their green bodies are sometimes found in dark corners among crowds of clinging mosquitoes—a friend and a foe of man resting together through the months of cold.

When this cold is replaced by spring's warmth, the lacewings are soon abroad. Among the herds of developing plant lice, the aphis-lions, which appear from their stalked eggs, soon range up and down infested plants waging war again in the gardener's behalf.

Members of the *Neuroptera* order number more than 4600 species in the world. About 340 of them inhabit North America.

Some, like the dobson fly and the alder fly, have aquatic larvae. The immature forms of the dobson flies lurk under rocks in swift-flowing streams and prey upon the aquatic larvae of other insects. They are known as hellgrammites or conniption bugs and are highly favored as bait for bass fishing. The females of the alder flies cement large masses of tiny cylindrical eggs to leaves that overhang streams. As the baby insects hatch they drop into the water and commence an aquatic life that lasts until they emerge as winged adults. Far different is the surroundings of another, and more familiar, member of the *Neuroptera* order, the ant lion. In its immature form, it excavates round pits in the loose sand and buries itself at the bottom with only its sharp jaws, like a pair of calipers, projecting. There it waits for some running ant to stumble into its pit and come sliding down with the loose sand. The adult ant lion, flying rather weakly on four long, filmy wings, resembles at first glance a slender damselfly. A widely used common name for this relative of the lacewing fly is the doodle bug.

9. THE LIFE OF
THE MONARCH BUTTERFLY

LEPIDOPTERA

THE black-and-orange wings of the monarch butterfly are familiar from central Canada to the lowland bayous of Louisiana; from Long Island to the rocky California headlands at Monterey. They carry this far-ranging insect up almost to the timberline of the Rockies; out over the Great Dismal Swamp and the Florida Everglades; above the skyscrapers of New York and Chicago, Denver and Los Angeles, and even far from shore over the oceans.

No butterfly is more widespread in the United States. No other butterfly is known to more Americans.

Originally, the monarch was a New World insect. It was an inhabitant only of the Americas, North, South, and Central. In recent decades, however, riding on its own wings or carried by commercial shipping, it has spread to Europe, to Hawaii, to Java, Sumatra, and the Philippines. Wherever the milkweed flourishes, there the monarch can make its home. It was only after milkweed

139

was introduced into Hawaii that the monarch appeared and became established. The larvae of this butterfly dine on milkweed and on nothing that is not related to milkweed. They will die of starvation in the presence of acres of luscious leaves if those leaves do not belong to the *Asclepias* or closely related dogbane family.

Some other butterflies have just as limited a range in diet when they are larvae. The great spangled fritillary, a gorgeous creature familiar in many parts of the United States and decorated with more than a score of glinting silver spots on each hind wing, eats, in its immature larval form, nothing but the leaves of violets. On the other hand, other butterflies relish many foods. The spiny larvae of the familiar "thaw butterfly," the dusky, cream-bordered mourning cloak that hibernates in hollow trees and odd crannies and flutters about open glades during winter warm spells, will dine with equal appetite on poplar, elm, or willow trees. The anglewings devour nettles or hops or elm leaves. Once started on one kind of leaves, however, these larvae rebel at being switched to another kind of fare.

The story of the monarch's life, except for a few individual eccentricities like its preference for milkweed, is much like that of other butterflies. Its biography is, in the main, the biography of all members of the *Lepidoptera* order. Both the moths and the butterflies have a complete metamorphosis. They live in four different forms. Only the final, or adult stage, is the winged, far-wandering creature which is so widely known.

The first act in the four-act drama which is the life of the monarch is represented by the pale green egg. I have seen more than 250 of these eggs deposited on a window-screen by a captive female butterfly. They were all laid within an area of eight square inches. Under normal conditions, however, the eggs of the monarch are widely scattered. I have never found more than one egg on a leaf and there are usually no more than two or three deposited on the same plant. The egg is cemented, in most instances, to the underside of the leaf near the midrib. Later in the season, the female sometimes lays her eggs directly on the flowers of the milkweed.

140

The eggs, looking like green-tinted drops of dew, are attached to the pedicel of the flower.

This resemblance to a tinted dewdrop is shared by the eggs of numerous other butterflies. In fact, naturalists of Roman times believed that butterfly eggs were actually formed from dew. Pliny the Elder maintained that the butterfly had the following dainty origin: A drop of dew settled on a radish leaf in the spring. This dewdrop hardened in the heat of the sun. From it came a little grub which eventually gathered "a hard husk or case about her" and within it changed into a butterfly.

Act I of the drama of the monarch is relatively short. It lasts, normally, but four or five days. Then the shell of the egg opens and a dark midget of a caterpillar appears. It sets to work devouring the empty shell from which it has just crawled. Then, if—as is usually the case—it finds itself on the underside of a milkweed leaf, it bites into the plant tissues and tunnels upward until it reaches the upper surface of the leaf. Its third meal, as well as its thirtieth and its three-hundredth, consists of the tissues and juices of the milkweed. It tastes nothing, during the rest of its larval life, but such fare. If the egg has been laid on the flower of a milkweed, the hatching larva eats its way downward into the flower and only later turns to its staple fare of milkweed leaves.

Scientists have played tricks on monarch caterpillars. They have enclosed other kinds of vegetable tissues between leaves of milkweed and have fed these sandwiches to the larvae. In consequence, they have learned that the caterpillars have excellent senses of taste. As soon as the undesired vegetable matter reached their mouths, they quickly spit it out. The caterpillars also have good senses of smell. Various laboratory tests have proved this. Whenever milkweed leaves were perfumed or treated with methyl alcohol, thus eliminating their natural odor, the larvae ignored them. On the other hand, when leaves of various kinds were placed on the other side of a fine wire-gauze, which prevented the monarch caterpillars from reaching the food, they would pass on over all other leaves and stop above milkweed as soon as they reached it.

141

They would remain there, making searching movements with their heads as though puzzled by their inability to reach the food they smelled.

To our eyes, a caterpillar appears to be the most unenlightened of creatures. Yet, it is admirably equipped for its mode of life. Even though it has no detectable ears, it senses sound vibrations and will cease all motion and remain perfectly still at certain sudden sounds. Hairy caterpillars do this by means of their stiff spines. When such hairs are loaded with water droplets or flour, the caterpillars appear to lose their ability to catch sound vibrations. A monarch larva is relatively hairless. How can it detect the vibrations? The most widely accepted theory is that there are very small hairs on its body which react to sound.

Near the head and the tail of the monarch larva there are a pair of dark, whiplike appendages which the creature can lash or wave about at will. These whips are the caterpillar's only defense against the great menace of its larval life—the parasites which deposit their eggs in the tissues of its body. As the swishing tail of a cow drives off the biting flies, so the lashing whips of the monarch larva will sometimes frighten away its would-be attackers.

The days of the larva are spent in almost continuous feeding. Act II in the drama is almost one endless meal. The creature's one aim is to devour as much milkweed as possible and to grow as fast as it can. During its caterpillar life it does all its growing; it is then that the larva stores up the tissues which are later re-formed into the body, the wings, the legs of the adult monarch.

When it is not eating, it is usually clinging motionless to the protected underside of a leaf. But these resting periods are soon succeeded by a fresh attack on the milkweed plant. Its cutting jaws snip out mouthfuls of the food in rapid succession. I have observed a monarch larva feeding long after dark. It seems to feed during hours of the night as well as during the day.

This is its story for the duration of the second act. For a dozen days, on the average, it devotes itself to concentrated eating, molting from time to time as its size increases. As soon as it has molted, it devours all the skin it has just shed with the exception of the head. Then it falls to on the milkweed leaves as though to make up for lost time.

How many molts the caterpillar makes is a subject for dispute. Some authorities say four; others, three. At any rate, the final molt brings the caterpillar to its maximum size. Brilliantly marked with stripes of yellow, black, and green, it is about two inches in length. Its days of feeding are nearing their end; its larval life is almost over. Now, the caterpillar grows restless; it wanders about; it travels sometimes as far as 300 feet from the plant on which it last was feeding. This instinctive journey of the larvae before they pupate helps spread them over a greater area and thus makes an accident that would wipe out all the chrysalises in a single blow more unlikely.

The curtain now rises on Act III. Spinning silk from glands in its mouth, the monarch caterpillar forms a tab on the underside of a leaf or twig and attaches its tail to this silken support. Hanging downward, with its head curled up so its body forms a capital J in the air, the larva slowly alters in form. Its skin splits and works upward and off its body. The emerging pupa, or chrysalis, hardens in the air and remains dangling from the support by a black, thread-like attachment. Butterflies always produce such bare chrysalises. Moths, on the other hand, frequently surround the pupa case with a cocoon of spun silk.

Most butterfly chrysalises are drab-looking objects designed to merge with their backgrounds and remain as inconspicuous as possible. The monarch chrysalis is an exception. It is one of the most beautiful objects in nature. Smooth and waxy and of the richest shade of green, it is decorated with spots of shining gold. Suggesting something out of a jewelry shop, instead of something just produced by a caterpillar, it remains, day after day, hanging motionless and apparently dead. As a matter of fact, it is a living, changing organism, unlike either the caterpillar which preceded it or the adult butterfly which will follow it.

It absorbs oxygen and it gives off heat. The noted American lepidopterist, Samuel H. Scudder, once tried an experiment in the middle of August in a room where a carefully graded thermometer indicated a temperature of 68.25 degrees F. When he placed the chrysalis of a monarch butterfly against the bulb, the mercury in the thermometer rose to 68.5 degrees. When the chrysalis was removed, the mercury returned to its former reading.

Under abnormal weather conditions, the length of Act III may be as short as two days or as long as twenty-one. The normal number of days in the chrysalis is twelve. Frequently monarchs emerge just before a thunderstorm. During the latter days of its pupal life, the monarch's form and coloring begin to become apparent. The green fades from the chrysalis. The golden spots tarnish and grow dull. The veining of the wings and the markings of the butterfly's body can be clearly seen through the almost transparent shell of the pupa-case.

At the dramatic moment when the climax of the creature's life, the emergence as a winged adult, arrives, the shell of the chrysalis is rent at the bottom. Out creeps the emerging butterfly. It crawls from its transformation chamber head downward. Climbing up the swaying, empty husk of the chrysalis, it clings to the leaf or twig while its wings expand and harden. The final act, Act IV, of this insect drama has arrived.

Watching closely, you can see the form of the newly emerged butterfly alter from moment to moment. Pushed out by blood pumped from the insect's heart, the wings gradually expand. The body of the butterfly grows less plump. Its soft outer skeleton hardens. Its proboscis begins to uncoil and coil again as the insect locks together the two parallel parts of which this sucking tube is formed. Then, for a long time, the creature clings motionless as though regaining its strength.

Without a blemish, it gleams in the sunshine, its wings thatched with an infinite number of flattened scales that overlap like the shingles on a roof. These scales form the "dust" which comes off on your fingers when you handle one of these butterflies. Only on the wings of moths and butterflies are such scales found. The name of the order which includes these insects, *Lepidoptera,* means "scaly-winged."

If the newly emerged monarch is a male, its hind wings will carry a special pocket of scent scales. These hollow scales are connected with glands which give off a distinctive perfume. Many other male butterflies are similarly scented. The perfume of a male tiger swallowtail is said to resemble that of honey; the scent of a cloudless sulphur suggests violets; that of a monarch the faint perfume of faraway honeysuckle. Such scents, so delicate most human noses can catch but faint traces of them, are believed to play a part—like the bright plumage and the songs of birds—in attracting mates. In the case of the monarch, the scent scales form a dark enlarged spot on each rear wing along one of the veins. Males can be told from females at a glance by looking for such spots on the hind wings.

The wings of both male and female monarchs have another characteristic which has interested naturalists for generations. This is their striking, contrasting pattern which makes them easily seen. These brilliant wings are more than adornments. They are warnings to insect-eating birds to keep away. The exact opposite of protective coloring, their purpose seems to be to attract attention, to let all birds know they are the wings of a monarch. For these insects have an evil-tasting blood which nauseates the bird that tries to eat them. By warning inexperienced birds away, the wings of the insect protect it from attack. Otherwise, in learning that the monarch is not good to eat, birds would kill or injure numbers of the insects. Its "aggressive coloration" is an advertisement; and, for the monarch, it pays to advertise.

A notable and oft-cited instance of "mimicry" among insects which already has been mentioned, is connected with these flaunting wings of the monarch. A butterfly of a different family, the viceroy, an insect with entirely different history and habits, rides about on wings that have almost exactly the same pattern as those of the monarch. Its egg, its caterpillar, its chrysalis are different. Its body contains no nauseating fluids. Yet, because it looks like a monarch, it, too, is immune from the attacks of birds. As the New England entomologist Clarence Weed once put it: The viceroy is a sheep in wolf's clothing. The advertising of the monarch aids it, too. It thrives through mistaken identity.

But to return to the newly emerged monarch, clinging to its support in the sunshine. One curious thing that you notice, particularly if the insect is a male, is that it appears to have four legs instead of six. Its front pair of legs is short and atrophied. These legs are carried close to the underside of the thorax with the ends hanging down. The forelegs of the males are even shorter than those of the females. In both walking and clinging, the monarch—unlike most other familiar butterflies—uses only four of its six legs.

On these four legs, the emerged butterfly rests for an hour and a half or two hours while the chitin shell of its body hardens. As the wings become stiff and strong, the instinct to use them asserts itself. Before they take to the air, some butterflies and moths flutter their wings for a considerable time, or keep them trembling for minutes on end. That, however, is not the monarch's way. In one sudden, bold leap—without warning—it flaps into the air and sails away. During its first instant in a new element, it rides the air currents like a veteran. The monarch's crawling days and its dormant days are past. It is now a brilliant creature of the air.

Follow one of these new-born butterflies across some hillside weedlot rich in blooming plants, and you will see it alight on flower after flower. Its thirst for nectar seems endless. During the first three days of its adult life, the monarch spends most of its time in feeding. It seems to have brought with it the appetite of the caterpillar, only now its sole source of nourishment is nectar. Its coiled, hollow, pumping-tube of a tongue is its only means of obtaining food. No adult butterfly or moth damages foliage; it is always in the caterpillar stage that these insects harm vegetation.

At the end of three days of feeding, the adult monarch seems satisfied. It begins the wandering which is characteristic of its kind. From time to time, it stops for a sip of nectar; but most of its

146

waking hours are spent in drifting from field to field. Its manner of using its wings is well adapted to far-ranging flights. Unlike many of the smaller butterflies which flutter continuously while on the wing, the monarch has an easy, effortless mode of flight. It resembles the actions of a man on skates. It gives a flap or two and then a long coast; then flaps again and coasts. When alarmed, it attains considerable height and speed by beating its broad wings without a pause. But its normal "cruising" speed requires a minimum of effort.

Dusk is usually settling over the summer landscape when a monarch alights for the night. Long after many other butterflies are settled within the protection of some tussock or weed clump, it is on the wing.

Another peculiarity of its flying habits has given the monarch such nicknames as the storm king and the storm fritillary. In that tense calm before a summer thunderstorm, it is especially active. It sails about in the sultry air, beneath the mounting thunderheads, seemingly stimulated by the electric tenseness in the atmosphere. These sturdy fliers also seem to revel in boisterous winds. I have seen them beating head-on into gusts, riding them upward in sudden rushes like windblown leaves.

It is this combination of characteristics—a bent for wandering and the ability to be abroad in many kinds of weather—that enables the monarch to make its spectacular annual migration to the South. This autumn journey carries some of the insects from the lower end of Hudson Bay to the Everglades of Florida or the cypress swamps of Louisiana—an aerial trek of more than 1000 miles achieved on four-inch wings.

During summer days, the butterflies are drifting individualists. But when the chill of approaching autumn comes, they begin to grow sociable. They gather in knots and flocks and then in larger bands. This is the initial step in a mass migration which, for regularity and extent, is unique among American insects. During the shortening days of autumn, they stream southward. On some occasions, they pass a given point all day long like a flowing river of insects. The advancing front of the migrating monarchs is often miles wide. The numbers of the insects are so vast that trees on which they settle for the night appear covered with massed brown leaves.

With the wind, against the wind, across the wind; above the traffic of city streets, out over winding rivers and the long right-of-way of railroads, across wild stretches of swamp and woodland, the migrating monarchs journey on. Day after day, they work southward. More than half a thousand observations attest to their mystifying ability to hold to their course on the long voyage south. This ability is even more amazing when we consider that not one member of that vast horde of insects pouring through the sky has made that journey before. Instinct leads them on a flight which carries them as far as the annual migration journey of many a Canada goose.

Along the Atlantic Coast, the Mississippi Valley, and the Pacific Coast, monarchs seem to have their major flyways. In the East, they come down from New England, follow along the outer shore of Long Island, and cross over to the New Jersey mainland, just as do the migrating birds. Deep-sea fishermen often see monarchs many miles from shore, crossing the expanse of water from Long Island to New Jersey.

In the late 1880's, Dr. M. G. Ellzey, of Washington, D.C., observed one of the greatest mass movements of the monarchs ever reported from the region of Chesapeake Bay. By seven o'clock in the morning, the insect hosts were already coming in from the wide stretch of water, flying steadily into the teeth of a stiff breeze. The butterflies were moving at different altitudes ranging from about 100 feet above the ground to a height at which they appeared hardly larger than flies. Dr. Ellzey calculated that the insects were traveling at a speed of approximately twenty miles an hour. By noon, the bulk of the flight was over. However, individual monarchs and straggling bands kept passing over the spot for days afterwards.

Some seasons are particularly favorable for the production of large numbers of monarchs. During such years, the migration

148

flocks reach spectacular proportions. In 1928, one flock of the kind appeared over the Cascade Mountains, in the State of Washington. Game wardens, looking away from the top of a high ridge, saw what they thought was a dark cloud approaching from the horizon. When it reached them, it proved to be an immense flock of brown-and-black milkweed butterflies moving south. So vast were the numbers of these insects that the game wardens estimated the flock was ten or fifteen miles long and three or four miles wide. How many billion insects it contained no one will ever know.

At the conclusion of the long aerial trek to the South, the butterflies separate and spend the winter months among the flowers of the Gulf states. In California, their migration carries them only part way down the coast. At Pacific Grove, on the Monterey peninsula, they collect each winter night on certain trees near the coast. They have been sleeping in these same butter-fly trees for so long that no one remembers when they began. A few years ago, the City Fathers of Pacific Grove set these trees aside as a unique insect sanctuary. A municipal law protects both the butterflies and the trees from harm.

How monarchs return north in the spring is still something of a riddle. They do not move up the map, as they went down, in vast flocks. Females, flying low above the ground, and with their wings tarnished so they attract little attention, are seen in fields around Washington, D.C. early in spring. And a new crop of brilliant butterflies always appears in northern states by mid-summer. It is known that the cold of winter kills all the eggs, all the larvae, and all the pupae in the North. How do the adults repopulate their northern summer homeland?

There are three hypotheses to explain the return of the monarchs. One is that they fly north unobtrusively, with most of the tarnished insects females. A second theory is that the migrating insects come north in a series of waves, the females laying their eggs on milkweed as it appears and the brood thus produced moving farther north to repeat the process. A third suggestion, held by only a few scientists, is that some monarchs may hibernate like the mourning cloak butterflies and from these insects the first broods of the summer are produced. At any rate, we know that the monarchs return with the warmth of spring and that they begin their new cycle of life as soon as the milkweed is well established.

There are, in the summer season, about three broods of monarchs. The average life-span of the insect during the summer appears to be from a month to six weeks. The last brood of the year makes up the bulk of the migrants that go south. They live beyond the normal summer span; they are apparently the longest-lived of the succession of butterfly generations.

The common names of the monarch are many. They range from The Queen-of-Spain butterfly to the milkweed butterfly, the wanderer, and the Bermuda butterfly. Even in its scientific names, there is more than ample variety. It is called *Danaus plexippus* in some books, *Anosia plexippus* in others, *Danaus menippe* in others, and *Danaus archippus* in still others—to the complete confusion of the amateur naturalist.

The only available comfort in such a situation is that once offered by Dr. Frank E. Lutz. "If," he advised in his volume, *A Lot of Insects*, "you notice that the scientific names used here are not quite the same as those used in some other book, do not worry. This matter of names is so confused that there is an international commission to deal with it, but international commissions must, apparently, be given plenty of time. Meanwhile, we should keep calm and act as though an insect by any other name is just as interesting." The most widely accepted scientific name for the monarch at the present time is *Danaus plexippus*.

Of the world's 113,000 species of *Lepidoptera*, North America has about 10,000 species. No other order contains such beauty of color and form as is exhibited by these butterflies and moths. The largest of the American moths appear in spring. They are the great silk moths, the cecropia, the luna, and the Polyphemus. The luna, pale green in color, is unique for its long ribbon tails; the Polyphemus for the large staring eye-spots on its hind wings. As is the case with most moths, these nocturnal insects are most often seen at lights. All of the large silk moths overwinter in cocoons, emerge in the spring, live but a short time, and never eat as adults. The other species of American moths are legion. They range from the sphinx moths that hover like hummingbirds before trumpet-shaped flowers in the dusk to those curious mimics, the clearwings, that sometimes resemble wasps and often suggest some creation of the dry-fly tier's art. At the lower end of the size-scale are the tiny *microlepidoptera* that appear hardly larger than houseflies. The larvae of moths, feeding on forest leaves and agricultural products, are among the most destructive of the insects. The caterpillars of the gypsy moth, a beautiful creature in its adult form, are notorious for their ravages among New England shade and woodland trees.

The butterflies are more familiar to the average person than the more numerous moths because they are on the wing during the daytime while the moths, as a rule, fly at night. All the tints of the rainbow appear on the wings of the butterflies. In the United States, these insects run the gamut from midget hairstreaks and tailed blues to the gaudy tiger swallowtails and the great spangled fritillaries. It is in the tropics, however, that the butterflies present their most striking and gorgeous hues. Because of their beauty and economic importance, the members of the *Lepidoptera* order, the moths and butterflies, have probably been collected and studied more extensively than the insects of any other group.

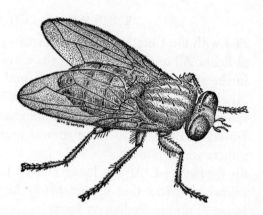

10. THE LIFE OF
THE HOUSEFLY

DIPTERA

WHEN Theodore Roosevelt returned from his South American expedition to the Amazon, he was asked:

"What was the most dangerous animal you encountered on your trip?"

He replied without hesitation:

"An insect!"

Just as the malarial mosquito is an outstanding menace of the tropics, so the housefly is a menace in more northerly lands. It cannot bite or sting. It carries no venom. Yet this quarter-of-an-inch insect has been called the most dangerous animal within the borders of the United States.

If you like your villains painted black, without any trace of gray tones, the life of *Musca domestica* will be just to your taste. For the housefly is an insect villain with hardly a drop of redeeming virtue.

It is a lover of pollution and filth and it provides a transportation system for a whole army of germs. Millions of bacteria and protozoa ride about on the bodies of flies. Scientists who have examined these insects microscopically have found on them germs and pathogens of such dreaded diseases as Asiatic cholera, amoebic dysentery, typhoid fever, diarrhea, tuberculosis, leprosy, gonorrhea, erysipelas, gangrene, and bubonic plague. It is a list calculated to produce shivers in any susceptible reader. In none of these diseases, however, is the housefly the only transmitter. In contrast, malaria is carried only by the mosquito; typhus fever is transmitted only by the louse. In carrying the plague, lice become sick. But the housefly carries its many germs lightly. Although some enter its system and are spread through its saliva and its excrement, left behind as "fly specks," its own health is not affected.

The fact that a housefly is a hairy insect and that it has sticky pads on the bottoms of its feet, which aid it in walking up windowpanes and on the ceilings of rooms; the fact that it is active and far-ranging; the fact that it is filled with insatiable curiosity, all make it a greater menace to human health than it otherwise would be. Most of the germs it transports ride on the hairs of its body or the sticky pads of its feet.

Two American entomologists, who made a careful census of the bacteria on 414 different houseflies, discovered that the average number on an insect was 1,250,000. That million and a quarter total of death-carrying hitchhikers was multiplied five times in the record number of germs found on a single fly. On this insect, the research workers counted 6,600,000 disease-producing bacteria.

A housefly that is here today may be as far as thirteen miles away on a later day. Marked flies have shown that these insects are always on the move. And during its travels it goes slumming whenever possible. Stables, outhouses, the carcasses of decaying animals, garbage pails, and sewage plants are all highly to its liking. The germs accumulated along the way are dropped off en route, oftentimes on and around food.

In connection with food, the worst of the fly's habits is yet to be noted. The housefly has no jaws for biting. It must take all its food

153

in liquid form. Hence, when it alights on the chocolate frosting of a cake, it cannot bite out little chunks of the desired sweets. It has to dissolve the frosting in fluid and obtain it in that way through its sucking proboscis. The fluid employed is either its own germ-laden saliva or previously swallowed liquid which it regurgitates and then swallows again after the sugar has been dissolved in it. This method of feeding increases greatly the germ-spreading menace of the housefly.

It is no wonder that this insect has been given such nicknames as the disease fly and the typhoid fly. Its activities are not confined to any one place or any one country. It is found throughout the world. We refer to it as the housefly; we link it in our minds with civilization and big cities. But, as a matter of fact, it has been found by explorers in remote regions, rarely frequented by man. Wherever there is filth in which to breed, there the housefly flourishes.

Piles of dung, especially piles of horse manure, are the chosen sites of its childhood. The mother fly places in such material her clusters of elongated white eggs. They are deposited in batches of from 100 to 150. Each female fly lays from two to seven batches. The average number of eggs deposited by a female housefly is about 500. The most fertile fly that science has had a chance to observe was one that laid twenty-one batches with a grand total of 2387 separate eggs.

Twenty-five housefly eggs, laid end to end, measure only one inch. Sometimes they hatch the same day they are laid. The shells split and out crawl the minute white grubs. The egg stage of a housefly lasts from six to thirty hours. The whole process of producing a new generation of houseflies, from the laying of the eggs to the appearance of the winged adults, may require, under favorable conditions, less than a week.

The maggot which appears from the egg and begins its rapid development, is shaped much like an old-fashioned powder horn. Its white body is large at one end and tapers almost to a point at the other. Curiously enough, it is the slender "tail" which, in reality, is the head of the larva. The grub bears no resemblance at all

154

to the adult fly. It is legless, footless and almost headless. In spite of these handicaps, it wiggles about within the warm mass of fermenting dung, seeking its food. As a rule, the larvae remain in the warm moist outer portions of the heap. The eggs are usually laid only in manure piles that are reached by the sun. One method of combating the housefly which has met with success has been to store stable refuse in dark pits or boxes. In such manure, the flies make no effort to deposit their eggs. The coming of the automobile, replacing the horse and eliminating stables in cities, has gone far in reducing the housefly population.

But in favorable situations, out-of-doors and in the sunshine, the eggs are laid in piles of decaying vegetable matter as well as in piles of manure. Maggots of houseflies show a definite temperature preference. When tested in the laboratory, they seek out places where the temperature ranges from sixty-two to sixty-nine degrees F. When a maggot is full-grown, however, it chooses a cooler place, preferring a spot where it is below forty-seven degrees.

An important reason why the growing larva chooses higher temperatures is that fermentation in the manure or decaying vegetation begins at about sixty-two degrees. The main food of the housefly larvae, it is believed, are the microorganisms which cause fermentation and decay. These increase most rapidly at higher temperatures. By its choice of food, the housefly larva loses a chance to compensate for the injurious activity of the adult insects. In the tropics, termites aid in the swift disintegration of fallen trees. The burying beetle, the ant and the flesh fly, all aid in the disappearance of waste matter. But the housefly can claim no such credit. It devours the organisms that hasten the disintegration of the refuse in which it lives. Its activity slows down, rather than hastens, the disappearance of this undesirable material. It works against the interests of man even in its earliest days.

To the maggot, the manure pile offers warmth and easy plenty. With its fellows, it tunnels about from one rich pasture to the next. The number of maggots in a single pile of horse manure is indicated by the fact that one economic entomologist found 458 housefly maggots in seven ounces of manure. In another test, Dr. Leland O. Howard discovered that one pound of stable manure would produce as many as 1200 flies. After being exposed to the egg-laying activity of the female flies for only four days, a half-ton pile of manure was sampled at various spots. From these samples, scientists estimated that the pile contained fully 400,000 fly larvae.

The immature flies all develop in the same manner. They eat steadily, grow rapidly, shed their skins in three molts, reach a length of from one-third to one-half inch, and then migrate to the drier, cooler parts of the mass where they change into pupae. This transformation is accomplished within the shed skin of the third molt. As this skin hardens, it becomes darker until it attains a chestnut hue.

The whole period of rapid growth and change recorded in the above paragraph may occupy a space of only four days. Under unfavorable weather conditions, it may be prolonged to fourteen days. Similarly, the time spent in the pupal form may be as short as three days or as long as ten. The climax of this period of rest, in either case, is the same.

The end of the brown puparium splits and out crawls the winged adult fly. From head to tail, it measures approximately one quarter of an inch. Compound eyes cover either side of its head, each eye composed of some 4000 six-sided lenses. Its thorax, or mid-body, is dusty gray. Four dark stripes run lengthwise along its top. The five segments of the abdomen are all covered with stiff hairs. The flight muscles within the thorax comprise about 11 per cent of the total weight of the insect.

The wings which they operate are transparent and strongly veined. Moving them at the rate of 330 times a second, a housefly can remain on the wing for surprisingly long periods of time. Behind the wings, on the insect's thorax, there are a pair of knobbed organs known as balancers or halteres. They whirl about at great speed, like the governors on a steam engine, when the insect is in flight. Many scientists believe these organs are the remnants of an extra pair of wings, such as bees and wasps possess, which the fly-

156

tribe has lost during the ages of evolution. Two wings and two knobbed organs behind them are characteristic of all flies.

Below the body of the housefly are the six hairy legs which end in feet equipped with both claws and sticky pads. If the insect is walking on a table, it uses its claws to maintain its hold on its support. But if it is climbing up a windowpane or is walking upside down on a tiled ceiling of a bathroom, it employs other means. The pads behind the claws are covered with short, hollow hairs which excrete a sticky fluid. Wherever the insect plants its feet, when the pads are exposed, they adhere. A fly walking across a ceiling is literally sticking in place each time it takes a step. And each time it pulls its foot away, it is bringing with it all the germs which lay on the spot where it has stepped.

When laboratory workers let a housefly walk back and forth across a plate of nutrient gelatine, they were able to demonstrate dramatically the danger of its sticky pads. Wherever the fly had planted its feet, white "tracks" appeared after the lapse of a few days. The tracks were formed of the rapidly growing bacteria and disease germs left behind. This experiment made visible the invisible, revealed the infinite number of germs transported by the sticky pads of a housefly's feet. Using food as a footmat, it transfers germs where they are most likely to do harm.

Besides carrying germs on the pads and the hairs, the legs of a housefly are used by that insect for tasting. The lower part of the leg contains organs of taste. As the insects walk about, laboratory tests have shown, they are able to tell by means of their legs when they are over food that suits their fancy.

A brownish yellow tint on the lower side of the abdomen is characteristic of the male houseflies. The females, in contrast, have a reddish tint. Another mark of difference is that the males have their compound eyes set closer together than the females. The females are sometimes less than sixty hours old when they are busy laying eggs. At other times, they are twenty-three days old before they mate and deposit their eggs. But even at the latter extreme, the generations of houseflies follow each other rapidly. It is the combination of a short life cycle and immense individual families which makes the housefly increase so abundantly.

In Massachusetts, a generation of houseflies will mature, under favorable conditions, in about fourteen days. In Washington, D.C., ten days is sufficient. Higher temperatures and plentiful food shorten the maturing time for the flies. In the latitude of Washington, Dr. Leland O. Howard reports, it is possible to have as many as fourteen generations of flies in one summer. The maximum for Massachusetts is given as eight.

But even by the eighth generation, a housefly which originally laid only 100 eggs and had only half of them hatch into females could, under ideal conditions, be the progenitor of 1,875,000,000,000 adults. Even more spectacular are the figures compiled by Prof. C. F. Hodge, during the excitement of the anti-fly campaigns of some decades ago. He showed that a single pair of houseflies, which began to reproduce in April, could, if all the flies lived, be the progenitors by August of 191,010,000,000,000,000,000 adults. He dramatized these figures still further by allowing one-eighth cubic inch for each fly and calculating the space the insects would take up. The descendants of this one pair of houseflies, he reported, would be sufficient to cover the earth with a layer more than three stories high!

Of course the catch, and a fortunate one for us, is the qualifying phrase "if all the flies lived." In real life, only a small proportion survive. Enemies of many kinds are ever on the attack. They make the theoretically possible increase of houseflies a nightmare that never comes true.

Man, with his swatters, his lethal insecticides, and his electrified screens plays the chief role in reducing the number of houseflies. Manure piles treated with hellebore or borax become death sites for the maturing maggots. Hosts of the larvae are destroyed by special maggot traps.

Even if none of these factors had entered into the story, natural checks and balances would still hold the flies to a small fraction of their possible numbers. Several wasp-like parasites prey both

158

upon the larvae and the pupae of the housefly. Spiders with their webs take a continual toll of the adults. Hornets prey upon houseflies. In pioneer America, settlers are said to have made capital of this latter fact.

Writing in 1840, the English entomologist, Westwood, quotes a portion from Hector St. John de Crevecoeur *Letters from an American Farmer* which relates to the habit of settlers who hung a hornet's nest in their homes in order to rid it of flies! That this is not a bit of hearsay or a flight of imagination is indicated by a still later record. Benjamin D. Walsh, an American entomologist, noted in 1869 that the wasps were called upon in pioneer days and that "they soon made a clearance of the obnoxious flies and so long as you do not meddle with them they will not meddle with you."

Almost microscopic red mites also aid in the war on houseflies. They sometimes almost cover the bodies of infested flies. Each mite has its little slender beak inserted in the body of the insect; each mite is draining away the blood and the vitality of its unwilling host.

Even smaller is an enemy which is probably the worst of all the foes of the housefly. It can be seen only through a microscope. This is a fungus spore. There are several kinds of fungi which bring wide destruction to the hosts of the housefly. Everyone, in late summer, has noticed flies seemingly frozen to the windowpane, a circle of whitish frost apparently holding them to the glass. The "frost" is fungus. Starting within the body of the fly, it grows outward in a sort of stem that reaches the windowpane and thus holds the dead insect in position. These fungus diseases are most active in late summer and autumn. They disappear with cold weather in December.

The life span of a healthy housefly can fall within a wide range. When a scientist kept 3000 well-fed houseflies in a cage, he found they lived for nineteen days on the average. Another laboratory worker reported that flies under his observation lived more than half again as long. Their span was thirty days. The longest life of any active housefly of which I have heard was more than twice this latter period. This Methuselah of the flies lived for seventy days.

As autumn advances, the flies become less active. When the mercury drops to forty-five degrees they cease to move about. Rarely can they survive temperatures below eighteen degrees. During these fall days of steadily lowering temperatures the insects, at times, seem hardly able to pull the sticky pads of their feet away from a surface on which they have been placed. They walk along a windowpane with diminishing strength, tugging at their feet as though they were walking in deep and sticky mud.

When winter settles down, the end of the housefly's tremendous fertility arrives. The insect is believed most often to overwinter as a larva or pupa. Occasionally it survives until spring as an adult. In large cities, almost all flies encountered in a house late in autumn are *Musca domestica;* but in small towns and country villages, there are other species as well. When Dr. Leland O. Howard made a census of wintering flies in Washington, D.C., he found that from 90 to 95 per cent were true houseflies. But when Dr. A. H. Morgan, of Mount Holyoke College, conducted a similar census in attic rooms in South Hadley, Massachusetts, she found only 65 per cent were houseflies. The rest were outdoor species which had come indoors late in fall.

Among the flies which Dr. Morgan discovered were both males and females. It is usually the fertilized female, she reports, that survives until spring. Such hibernating insects, of course, live far beyond the normal span of the active summer flies. In warmer sections of the country, the housefly probably breeds slowly throughout the winter, speeding up in its development as soon as the temperature rises in the spring.

Besides *Musca domestica,* there are about 85,000 other species of two-winged true flies that have been described by scientists. More than 16,500 live in North America. They range from the swift antelope and deer flies of the Western plains to those slow and awkward daddy longlegs of the air, the crane flies. The mosquito is a fly and so are the midge and the gnat and the biting black fly of the north woods. One group of flies performs a beneficial service from man's viewpoint, by killing other insects—often mosquitoes. These are the fast, predaceous robber flies. They include numerous species, one of which is an almost perfect imitation of a furry bumblebee. Some flies, such as the *Tachinidae*, are parasitic on caterpillars; others, like the botflies, parasitize sheep and similar animals; others, like the wheat midge and the notorious Hessian fly, cause damage to growing grain; still others, the so-called flesh flies, consume decaying animals. There are stiletto flies and hump-backed flies and big-headed flies. Each has habits unique to itself. Dance flies vibrate up and down, sometimes in flocks so vast their tiny wings produce a sound like "a distant waterfall." Hover flies hang in mid-air for minutes at a time as though supported by a thread, and the so-called peacock flies parade up and down with their spotted wings lifted and waving about. One species, the red-eyed fruit fly, *Drosophila melanogaster*, has played an important part in the advance of our knowledge of heredity and genetics. It can be bred easily in the laboratory and its generations follow each other in swift succession, thus speeding up evolution and shortening the time required for long-range experiments.

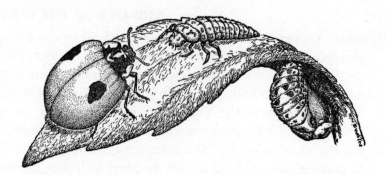

11. THE LIFE OF
THE LADYBIRD BEETLE

COLEOPTERA

AROUND THE world the ladybird beetle is a popular insect. In France it is believed to bring fine weather. In England the sight of numerous ladybugs in spring is supposed to indicate heavy crops. In pioneer America a ladybird beetle hibernating in the house over winter was considered a harbinger of good luck. And in Central Europe peasant girls caught ladybugs and let them crawl across their palms. This rite was supposed to insure their marriage within the year.

The insect's common names, such as ladybird, ladybug, ladycow, ladyfly, and ladycock, all have come down to us from the distant past. They reflect the fact that the insect was dedicated to Our Lady, the Virgin Mary. This long religious association is also indicated by the fact that Swedish peasants refer to the beetles as "the Virgin Mary's Golden Hens" and farmers in France call them "the Cows of the Lord."

162

The veneration and high esteem in which the ladybird beetle is held has a solid foundation. These insects *do* help bring good crops; they *do* aid in bringing good luck to farmers—even though not in the manner the superstitious believe.

It is as consumers of agricultural pests, both in their immature and adult stages, that the ladybugs make themselves invaluable. It is by their insatiable appetites for plant lice, potato-beetle eggs, and scale insects that they merit the good will they have built up through the ages. Approximately 150 of the 2000 known species of ladybird beetles are found in the United States. One is the black sheep of the family, an insect with the appropriate species-name of *corrupta*. This is the spotted bean beetle. It is a ladybug but it spends its time chewing up bean leaves instead of agricultural pests. The bean beetle is the skeleton in the *Coccinella* closet.

A number of ladybirds have been welcome immigrants to our shores. They have been introduced intentionally, particularly on the Pacific Coast, to fight insect pests. One of the most spectacular successes that economic entomologists have ever had in fighting one insect with another insect had as its star performer an unassuming little ladybird beetle brought from Australia. Hardly more than an eighth of an inch in length and looking like a small spotted pill cut in half and placed flat-side-down, it has been worth a million times its weight in gold to the orange-growers of the West Coast.

Shortly after the close of the Civil War, the destructive cottony cushion scale appeared in California citrus groves. Before 1890, it had killed hundreds of thousands of trees. The whole citrus industry of the state appeared on the verge of being wiped out. Then a small event, thousands of miles away, turned the tide in favor of the fruit-growers.

On the fifteenth of October, 1888, Albert Koebele, a representative of the Bureau of Entomology of the U.S. Department of Agriculture, noticed a small ladybug feeding on some cottony cushion scale in a garden in North Adelaide, Australia. He shipped twenty-eight of the beetles to the United States. Other shipments followed. The earliest of the Australian beetles to arrive were placed on an

infested tree which was surrounded by a tent. They fed and reproduced. In a short time the tree was entirely cleared of the scale
insects. The tent was taken away and the beetles spread to other
trees. Colonies were forwarded to many parts of the state. Hundreds
of thousands of the industrious beetles were soon working from
sunrise to sunset battling the scale-insect pests.

So valuable was the work of the beetles that, when there was
some question about the insects being able to live through the
winter months, special glass houses were built around infested
orange trees within which the imported beetles could be kept.
Soon, however, it was found that the ladybugs were well able to
take care of themselves the year around. The total cost of importing
the beetles from Australia was $1500. That modest investment
saved an industry which has brought hundreds of millions of dollars
to California during succeeding years.

The commoner species of American ladybird beetles, usually
clad in a polkadot dress of black spots on a reddish background,
are known to every gardener. Because they have done such valiant
work of destruction among plant-lice clusters, the beetles sometimes have suffered at the hands of those they are helping most.
Ignorant farmers have seen them among the massed bodies of the
aphides and have jumped to the conclusion that the beetles are the
parents of the plant lice. In the face of all arguments, they continued to kill the ladybugs in an effort to get rid of the aphides.
Similarly, English rose-growers, at one time, blamed aphis-wolves,
the lizard-shaped children of the ladybird beetles, for the presence
of aphides on their bushes. Wherever they saw clusters of the "green
flies" they also saw the aphis-wolves. Instead of appreciating the
labors of these insect-friends of theirs, they blamed them for all
their troubles.

The life of the ladybug is, like that of all insects having a complete metamorphosis, a play in four acts. The eggs are laid in the
crevices of bark or on the underside of some protected leaf. A
female ladybird beetle will deposit as many as 200 eggs. From these
eggs appear minute creatures that resemble closely the larvae of
164

the lacewing fly. However, instead of being blackish, their tapering lizard-like bodies are slaty or purplish and decorated with spots of red and blue and black. Running about on six slender legs, these aphis-wolves spend their days hunting and devouring innumerable plant lice.

In an hour one of these immature beetles will destroy as many as forty aphides. The aphis-lion drains away the vital juices of its victims; the aphis-wolf chews up their bodies and swallows them. These young beetles also consider insect eggs a special delicacy. Coming upon a cluster of eggs deposited by some other insect, they will begin at one side and work through to the other side, consuming every egg as they go. Both the immature beetles and the adults have this liking for eggs. By devouring thousands of those deposited by Colorado potato beetles, they do work of especial importance to American farmers in the potato-growing regions of the country.

After the passing of a few weeks, and the changing of its skin to accommodate its growth, the aphis-wolf attains its full size. It then hangs itself up by its tail to the surface of a leaf and there transforms into a short, stout chrysalis. The spotted shell of this pupa-case is shiny. Touch it with your finger and you find its surface is smooth, suggesting porcelain.

When this shell splits at the end of the insect's pupal days, the former aphis-wolf emerges as the winged adult beetle. It is in its fourth and final form. When the black-dotted shards are swung forward, the filmy, folded rear wings can carry the beetle through the air from bush to bush, from plant to plant, from tree to tree. These fan-like wings beat from seventy-five to ninety-one times a second while the insect is in flight.

Within the body of the adult beetle there is still a huge appetite for plant lice and insect eggs. But, as the adult is no longer growing, it requires less food and its consumption of aphides is smaller than that of the insatiable larva. An adult ladybug will consume about fifty plant lice at a sitting. Then it appears satisfied, at least for the time being. The larva never seems satisfied.

The enemies of ladybird beetles appear to be few. One of these is the bloodthirsty assassin bug. It drives the slender stiletto of its sucking beak into the beetle's body, thrusting home through a weak place in its armor, between the head and the body. When it has finished draining away the vital fluids, only the empty shell of the beetle remains.

For most other enemies, two ruses in the ladybug's bag of tricks are sufficient. The first of these is known to scientists as "reflex bleeding." By a sudden contraction of the abdomen, the beetle compresses its blood so strongly that it ruptures the skin at points of least resistance. These points are at the joints of its legs. In this way, the ladybird beetle is able to exude drops of yellowish, evil-smelling blood which repel would-be attackers.

A second trick helps preserve its life when it comes in contact with larger enemies, including man. This is playing 'possum. Like a number of other insects, the beetle will fall over as though dead when it is sufficiently alarmed. I have watched these shamming insects remain immobile for minutes. Then a tiny black leg would appear and soon the beetle would be struggling to right itself. In saving its life, the ladybug combines the stratagem of the skunk and the wiles of the opossum.

Within its unassuming little body, it also carries a number of curious attributes and abilities. For example, if you put a ladybird beetle on a large sheet of white paper, on which broad black bands have been placed, you will see the insect walk along the white section close beside the edge of a black band. The beetle will zigzag when the band zigzags and turn right angles when it turns right angles. By some little-understood instinct, it follows the line where black and white meet.

Another reaction which has interested laboratory workers is the fact that the insects seem sensible to the angle at which the rays of the sun strike their bodies. If a beetle is walking across a laboratory table which is illuminated by a single source of light and that light is switched off and another—located at a different point —is switched on, the insect will change its course until the light from the new source strikes its body from the same angle as before.

166

A number of other insects, including ants, respond in this way. It has been suggested that this instinctive behavior provides a "light compass" which keeps the creature orientated as it moves about on a sunny day.

The number of spots on the back of a ladybug varies according to the species. *Adalia bipunctata,* a common kind of ladybird beetle in Eastern states, has only two spots, one on each wing-case. Others have as many as fifteen spots. At one time, the seven-spotted ladybug was regarded by the superstitious as potent against toothache. Placed in a cavity, the crushed-up beetle was supposed to provide an almost instant cure.

In late-autumn days, the two-spotted beetle frequently seeks the interior of a country dwelling as its site for hibernation. When an overwintering beetle comes out on a day of thaw to fly about within the house, it shows uncanny ability, according to the British entomologist R. W. G. Hingston, for finding its way back to the very crevice it started from. This shows, he concludes, that the ladybugs possess a memory for places which lasts at least for several hours.

It is because of its hibernating habits that the ladybird beetle attracts special attention. I once received a letter from a naturalist in Michigan who had come upon tens of thousands of the beetles congregated on the sand and on stranded logs of the Lake Michigan shore. The insects become social in autumn. They mass together on rocks until sometimes the face of a huge mountain boulder will be red with their myriad bodies.

Out-of-doors, they hibernate in many places. Some seek old haystacks, others forest debris, others the loose siding of buildings, and still others find shelter beneath the bark on dead trees. Sometimes all the ladybugs in a mass will be of one species; at other times, two or three species will be represented. In forest mold, the beetles are found to a depth of half a foot. When one entomologist sifted a single square yard of the litter, he obtained 9808 hibernating ladybugs.

Where beetles hibernate under bark, they sometimes creep out into the warm sunshine during winter thaws. A Virginia entomologist, D. E. Fink, reports a curious circumstance in connection with this habit. A horse was left tied to a dead tree, under the bark of which beetles were bedded down for the winter. Attracted by the sunshine, they came out and then, using the bridle as a bridge, they crossed over to settle down on the warmth of the animal's body.

It is in the mountains of the West that the most spectacular massing of the beetles occurs. As autumn advances, untold millions of the insects fly upward from the valleys to hibernate in the crevices among the mountain rocks. This has given rise to one of America's most curious professions, that of ladybug prospector. Men seek out the masses of overwintering beetles and transport them down the mountainsides to sell them, at so much a gallon or an ounce or a thousand, to farmers and orchardists.

In one instance, in a V-shaped tract where two small mountain gullies met, at an elevation of 4000 feet above sea level, a single mass of hibernating beetles was estimated to contain 750,000,000 individuals. Forest rangers are always instructed to be on the lookout for such beetle-mines. When they are found, the insects are shoveled into sacks partially filled with excelsior and are carried like grain to refrigerators where they are kept for the rest of the winter at a steady temperature of about thirty-eight degrees F. From time to time, they are taken out into the sunshine to check any mold which might otherwise develop in the darkness of the refrigerating vaults.

With the coming of spring, the stored beetles go to market. Fifteen hundred ladybugs will weigh about one ounce. During a single spring, 100,000,000 of the beetles were distributed to orchardists and gardeners of the State of Washington alone. The price, some years ago, was $100 a million for the insects. A prescription used in the Imperial Valley of California to cure aphid-ridden fields is two ounces of ladybugs for each acre of ground. These 3000 beetles, laying their eggs and devouring plant lice on their own behalf, soon have the aphides under control.

No matter whether the overwintering adults arrive by fast parcel

168

post from one of the refrigerators where millions of the insects have been stored, or whether they creep from strawstacks or other hibernating places and take up life again by choosing their own fields of operation, spring finds them busily engaged among the plants of farms and gardens. The eggs which the females then lay begin anew the fourfold life cycle of a new generation of these beneficial beetles.

The beetles are the most widely distributed of all the insects. They comprise the largest of the insect orders. More than 26,500 species have been described from North America and more than 275,000 in the world. Infinitely varied, the vast numbers of the *Coleoptera* order include beetles of curious forms and surprising habits. Some of the relatives of the ladybug include the firefly with its glowing abdominal segments; the heavily armored stag beetles; the tumblebugs which, like their relatives, the scarabs of the Nile Valley, roll their spheres of dung along over pastures and barnyards; the weevils, including the notorious boll weevil of southern cottonfields, and the carrion beetles with their incredibly acute organs of smell which bring them from afar to feed on dead animals. There are minute beetles able to crawl through the eye of a needle and there are the heavy blundering May beetles, or Junebugs, that bang into the screens of lighted porches and bump along the glass of streetlamps. There are the swift-limbed tiger beetles, click beetles, blister beetles, long-horned beetles, diving beetles. There are beetles that spend their days whirling on the surface of still ponds, others that bore into lead cables, and still others that eat hair, tobacco, and carpets. There are even beetles that can live for a year without either food or water. Some species live in the ground, others in dry wood, others in anthills, others in caves, and others on the seashore. Each species among this multitude of beetles has its own habits, its own abilities, and its own special environment.

169

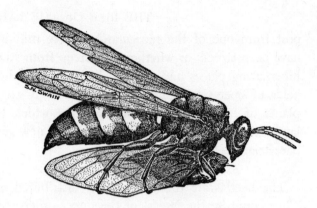

12. THE LIFE OF
THE CICADA-KILLER WASP

HYMENOPTERA

OUT OF THE earth, warmed by the sun and softened by the
early-summer showers, crawl the largest of the American wasps,
the cicada-killer, *Sphecius speciosus*. They emerge into the sunshine, their black and yellow bodies gleaming as though they had
been glazed in a pottery furnace. Each insect appears from a separate hole which it burrows upward from the subterranean chamber
in which it is born. Ahead of it stretches a summer of life and
intense activity which will end only with the coming of late autumn's cold. It is during the days of midsummer, when the air is
still and heavy and the shrill, far-carrying note of the cicada mingles
with the low reiterated calling of the rain-crow, that these wasps
are most in evidence.

It is then that they are searching the branches, flying this way
and that, digging feverishly in the dry earth, excavating burrows,
paralyzing prey, burying food for the future young, laying eggs,
170

working at top speed in their insect harvest-fields for the good of another generation, a generation which they will never see.

The cicada-killers belong to that group of solitary huntresses known as digger wasps. They include numerous brilliant-bodied insects, all of them having the habit of burying paralyzed prey in underground burrows to provide a store of food for their young. Many of these hunting wasps specialize in a single kind of insect. I always see *Chlorion ichneumoneum,* with its reddish-orange abdomen-stripe marking it at a glance, burying nothing but a certain kind of black-striped, long-horned grasshopper. The little green-banded digger, *Bembex spinolae,* brings in only flies. Another minute digger wasp specializes in aphides. And *Sphecius speciosus* is a hunter of cicadas alone.

Its life story is representative of the lives of these hunters and miners of the wasp world.

Emerged into the sunshine of the outer air, the newborn wasp flies to the nearest source of nectar. Although it hunts living prey and its larva is carnivorous, the cicada-killer never eats the insects it captures. It dines on more delicate fare, the sweet fluid of the flowers. Occasionally, these wasps vary this diet by imbibing sap, particularly if it is fermented. Bees, butterflies, ants, and flies, as well as wasps, gather excitedly about any gash in a treetrunk from which sap has oozed and become fermented. Butterflies sometimes consume so much fermented fruit juices in autumn that they become completely stupefied and can be caught without the use of a net. I have seen wasps following on the trail of a sapsucker, obtaining fluid which oozed from the holes the bird had made.

Those two noted observers of insect ways, Phil and Nellie Rau, of Kirkwood, Missouri, tell of watching a cicada-killer feeding on a mass of foamy sap exuding from a wound near the base of a large sunflower stalk. It was joined by others of its kind. "When we attempted to take them," the Raus write, "they expressed their indignation at being disturbed by the loudest noise that we have ever heard a wasp make. They buzzed about and always made attempts to return to their bacchanal." At other times, these same observers

171

found cicada-killers greedily drinking fermented sap of other kinds. The insects, they report, were "boisterously buzzing, bumping and whirling around at intervals."

Aside from such occasional lapses, the path of the cicada-killer wasp is strait and narrow. After mid-July, the females begin digging their burrows. They choose a dry location and prefer a clayey soil. If the site of their burrows is too damp, mold is likely to form on the buried cicadas. Close together, a score or more of the females will excavate their underground caverns. Sometimes the colonies of these solitary workers will exceed 100 individuals. I once visited a spot along a deserted red-clay road where, in the space of a hundred yards or so, 150 cicada-killers had dug their burrows. They make no effort to help each other; they remain solitary insects in their habits. But they are drawn together by the particularly favorable condition of the soil at certain spots.

If they do not help each other, rarely do they interfere with each other. They are peaceably inclined. A cicada-killer rarely uses its formidable sting—the longest possessed by any of our wasps—except for paralyzing its prey. Once in a while, a female will look into the entrance of a neighbor's burrow and occasionally one will go visiting, inspecting as many as half a dozen other burrows before she flies off on business of her own. On the twenty-fourth of August, when the season was getting late and the cicadas scarce, I once observed a second female interfere with a first as it approached its nest-site with a captured insect. This was the only instance of the kind I have ever seen. After a moment of flipping wings, the intruder left and the rightful owner of the cicada continued on her way.

Always, the burrow is prepared in advance of the cicada-hunting. It is excavated to a depth of several feet at a tremendous expenditure of energy. With masses of soft earth held in her forelegs and "under her chin," the wasp backs from the mouth of the tunnel. She walks with four of her six legs. In the early stages of her labors, she spreads out the excavated dirt by pushing it sidewise with her hind legs. Later on, the pile of dirt at the entrance becomes so great

172

that a kind of trough is formed through it by the passage of her body in dragging fresh loads of dirt from the interior. Her abdomen pushes a mound of the soft soil ahead of it in the manner of a bulldozer when she backs out during these latter trips. She appears to be carrying her body low to give her legs greater driving power and her abdomen more effective purchase on the dirt it is pushing.

The final step in completing the tunnel is the creation of several branching chambers near the bottom. These are large enough to hold one or two cicadas. It is always the annual cicada that stocks these underground larders, never the seventeen-year, or periodical, cicada. The hosts of these latter insects, with their red eyes and yellow-veined wings, appear only during the early weeks of summer. They have all died before the burrows of *Sphecius speciosus* are ready for their occupants. It is the greenish *Tibicen pruinosa* that, in Eastern states, most frequently is carried home by the wasps.

It used to be thought that the cicada-killers discovered their shrilling prey by the sound they made. This, however, apparently is not so. I have seen these wasps bring in several female cicadas in succession. And the females have no sound-making apparatus; they are completely voiceless. It is by sight, and not by hearing, that the cicada-killers detect the presence of their victims. Follow one of these hunting wasps in its search and you will see it hang beside a branch on blurring wings and then move helicopter-wise along it. Its great compound eyes are watching for the big-bodied insects which are its victims.

The success of this quest is often announced by a sudden, anguished change in the song of a male cicada. The shrill drone of the harvest-fly is replaced by a discordant screech followed by silence. With a swift jab of its sting, the black-and-yellow huntress has reached a nerve center in the singing insect's body. After that thrust, the cicada is paralyzed. Life goes on, but the insect never rouses from the comatose condition into which it has been thrown. If its conscious life is over, so also is its suffering. The fate which awaits it in the darkness of the underground cavern is without pain.

Usually, in the attack and the stinging of her prey, the cicada-

173

killer, together with her victim, tumbles headlong to the ground. If the wasp is near her burrow, she may drag the unconscious cicada along the ground to the entrance. Oftentimes, however, she is a considerable distance away. Grass-tangles and gullies, boulders and ditches, may lie between her and her goal. The cicada may weigh as much as six times as much as the wasp. Her wings usually can support the load only on a downward slant. She is unable to lift her burden into the air from the ground. Hence, she resorts to the following sagacious stratagem.

Firmly grasping her captured prey, she climbs upward along the trunk of a tree. Her speed, when dragging a load several times her own weight vertically up the treetrunk, is, surprisingly, almost as great as when she is traveling along level ground. Reaching a branch, some distance above the ground, the wasp pauses for a moment. Then she launches herself outward into space. Her wings blurr at top speed. On a long slant, like a swiftly descending glider, she heads for her distant burrow. Once launched, a wasp which is transporting an unusually light cicada can sometimes fly all the way to the site of her tunnel. But usually, several toilsome climbs and slanting descents are necessary.

The end of the flight brings wasp and prey bumping to the ground together. Even if it is comparatively close to its burrow, the wasp often mounts some bush or weed and launches itself into the air for a few seconds of flying. I have seen a burdened cicada-killer mount only a few inches above the ground on a clump of grass in order to whir into the air on a downward flight of less than a yard.

Watching one of these wasps dragging a cicada along the ground, you can understand this desire to gain distance by the swifter aerial route, even if for only a moment. On the ground it meets innumerable impediments. There are piles of weed-stems, dry and criss-crossed, which bar the way like mounds of logs. There are grass-tangle islands to skirt. There are thickets and vine-labyrinths. There are miniature mountains and gullies. All must be passed or surmounted before the goal can be reached.

Always, when dragging her prey along the ground, the cicada-
174

killer turns it over on its back and pulls it head-foremost. In this position, it slides along like a sled. Its feet are in the air and do not drag. Straddling its body, the wasp runs along in hurried, nervous dashes. Sometimes, it leaves its victim and runs on ahead, investigating the lay of the land and obstacles to be overcome. On its return, it often stings its prey all over again, as though afraid it might try to escape. Thus the black-and-yellow huntress progresses foot by foot. To cover fifty yards took one wasp I observed more than a quarter of an hour.

But, eventually, the entrance of the burrow is gained. Often the wasp, leaving the cicada outside, disappears within. She may be gone for several minutes while she investigates the interior. Then she appears again, grasps the cicada and moves swiftly into the burrow, dragging it underground. At this precise instant, a small parasitic insect, a midget that smells like slippery elm and has been circling about in the air or resting on a leaf in the sunshine nearby, sometimes darts toward the disappearing cicada. In a split second, it has deposited its egg upon the body of the paralyzed victim. Thus, in many cases, the labors of the cicada-killer wasp provide ample food for the progeny of the parasite after the tunnels have been filled in and the cicadas buried below-ground.

What happens in the darkness of the little chambers where these insects are secreted has been pieced together by various observations and researches. The cicada reaches its journey's end in a round cell about an inch and a half in diameter. The wasp attaches a single slender white egg to its body, always on the underside and near the front pair of legs. Sometimes a second cicada is added to the chamber; but only one egg is deposited within each miniature cavern. It was suggested by the famous government entomologist, C. V. Riley, that cells with two cicadas produce the larger females while those with only one cicada produce the smaller males.

From the eggs, attached to the living but paralyzed victims, hatch the larvae. The time spent in the egg-stage is only two or three days. The larvae immediately begin obtaining nourishment from the cicadas to which the eggs were attached. When the female wasp

175

paralyzes the cicada, she insures fresh food for the offspring. Her sting is the key to a kind of insect refrigeration system. Even in cases where the cicadas die, they seem to be preserved by the fluid which the sting of the wasp has injected.

Day by day, the larva increases its size. Feeding continues for a week or so. In this relatively short time, the immature wasp has attained its full growth and has consumed most of the food with which its underground chamber has been stored. The next two days are spent in producing, of silk and earth, the cocoon within which the larva retires for a dormant period that lasts for many months. A number of tiny holes, like pinpricks, in the side of the cocoon are thought to supply air to the imprisoned larva. Unlike the larva of a butterfly or moth, the immature cicada-killer wasp does not change directly into a pupa. It continues as a dormant larva all through the rest of the summer, all through autumn and winter and spring. It changes into a pupa only a short time before its emergence as an adult wasp early the following summer.

This emergence requires two steps. The wasp first has to break out of its pupal shell and then gnaw its way out of the cocoon. When this is accomplished, it is still imprisoned within the darkness of its underground chamber. A foot, or several feet, above it are the air and the sunshine of a world it is destined to enter. To reach this world, it must claw and push its way upward through the soil. Reaching the surface, it pauses for a moment then lifts into the air in flight. With this action, the wheel of the digger wasp cycle has completed a turn. A new generation has appeared. The cicada-killer's life story begins again at Chapter One.

That is, it does if the emerging insect is a female. If it is the smaller member of the species, a male, its existence is different. After drinking its fill of nectar, it will perch on some conspicuous bush or plant. It will circle and dart this way and that in the sunshine. Its days will be without labor. Its one purpose in existence is to fertilize some female so that the eggs laid on buried cicadas may hatch into the larvae that will insure the continuation of the species.

176

Males are more inquisitive, less absorbed in the activity of the day. They sometimes dart off to give chase to butterflies. Out of what appears to be nothing more than curiosity, they will investigate the approach of every stranger. When some small object, like a bit of orange peel, is tossed aloft, the male wasps will often dart at it like dragonflies and then return to their perches.

Life for both male and female cicada-killer comes to an end on some autumn night when the mercury drops to a point at which their tissues freeze. Before winter cold sets in, all the cicada-killers, as well as all of the cicadas, are gone. But underground, hidden from view, are the sleeping larvae of the wasps and the burrowing nymphs of the cicadas. Some of them will meet—the hunting and the hunted—in the long, hot days of another summer.

More than 100,000 species in the world, and nearly 15,000 in North America, belong to the *Hymenoptera* order. Instinct reaches its high-water mark in this group. No other six-legged creatures have as highly developed nervous systems or exhibit such adaptability and resourcefulness as members of the *Hymenoptera* order. It contains those insect aristocrats, the ants, wasps, and bees with their complex and efficient communal life.

It also contains numerous solitary insects of widely diverse habits. The familiar mud-dauber wasp stocks its masonry nest with paralyzed prey. The little leafcutter bee snips round sections from leaves and from them forms cuplike receptacles in which it places its eggs. *Megarhyssa lunator,* the large and strikingly marked ichneumon fly, drills through as much as several inches of wood to deposit her eggs in the tunnels of the *Tremex* sawfly larvae. Some tiny wasps produce galls on plants. Without one wasp to carry on fertilization, the whole California fig industry would collapse. The brilliant, metallic-hued velvet ants that hurry across open spaces on summer days are in reality wingless wasps with potent stings. Minute wasps, called fairy flies, specialize in parasitizing the eggs of other insects.

No one insect can represent the infinitely varied species of this

177

order, ranging as they do from solitary spider-hunters through the annual colonies of the bumblebees up to the complex, continuing insect cities of ants and honeybees. Because of this, and also because of the importance of this group and the fact that it presents the climax of insect development, the final two chapters will also concern *Hymenopterous* insects. The first will deal with life in the nest of the *Polistes* paper-making wasps and the second and final chapter will record the activity of dwellers in that underground metropolis, the anthill.

THE MONARCH butterfly is a famous insect traveler. It migrates in the autumn, sometimes winging its way southward for more than 1000 miles.

TWO STAGES in the life of the ladybird beetle have been caught in these photographs. Above, the larva devouring aphides; below, the adult beetle.

CARPENTER ants tunnel through solid wood, often in living trees, to produce the galleries that form their home. Unlike termites, they do not feed on wood.

THE LIVES of two wasps, one solitary, the other social, are represented here. Above, the cicada-killer with prey; below, *Polistes* wasps on their paper nest.

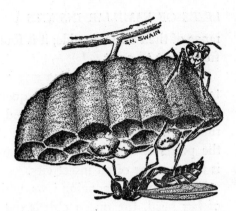

13. THE LIFE OF
THE PAPER-MAKING WASP

HYMENOPTERA

FAR DIFFERENT from the solitary labors of the cicada-killer is the communal activity of the social *Polistes* wasp. The hub of its existence is a flat, many-celled paper nest attached by a stem in some protected place, such as beneath the eves of a garage or under the roof of an old shed. The digger wasps are dwellers in the outlands; the *Polistes* is an urbanite, an inhabitant of a teeming insect city.

The narrative of its life is also the narrative of the rise and fall of the paper city with which its activity is so closely associated. This chronicle begins in the warmth of early spring; it ends in the frosts of autumn. The city of paper, which grows cell by cell during the summer months, is left empty and deserted when winter comes. The hosts of its inhabitants, with the exception of a few hibernating queens, are slain by the cold. The story of the city and the story of the wasps, in the main, is the record of a single summer. The range of the *Polistes* is wide; it is found scattered across the country from coast to coast.

As soon as the fluctuating weather of early spring settles down to sunny days, the hibernating queens crawl forth from crannies, from the interior of old barns and sheds, from under protecting rubbish. Sometimes two and even three queens labor together in the production of a nest. But, usually, each overwintering wasp is the founder of an insect city.

With powerful gouging jaws, which bite inward from the sides of her head, the queen chisels out bits of weathered wood and chews them into a soft pulp. These masticated fibers are mixed with her saliva. This combination forms the raw material of the world's first pulp-wood paper. The sheets of your daily newspaper were antedated millions of years by the pulp-wood walls of a wasp nest.

The initial cell of the nest is the "village square" of the insect community-to-be. Around it, in expanding rings, will be constructed the other cells. This original cell has the appearance of a long-stemmed goblet, hanging upsidedown. As the nest grows, the stem of this goblet will be strengthened from time to time. It is the central support of the whole nest. Even before a second cell is added, the queen lays an egg, cementing it to the inside of the inverted cup. From then on, her days will be spent in flying to weathered boards, old trees, bleached fenceposts, gathering the wood fibers from which she will shape the additional cells. As each is completed, an egg is placed within together with a little drop of nectar which shines like quicksilver when struck by the rays of the sun. This nectar is the first food of the tiny larva which hatches from the egg. The first larva to hatch is the inhabitant of the central cell.

By autumn, the nest may consist of two hundred or more of the six-sided paper cradles from which have come maturing wasps to swell the population of the metropolis. Of these cells, the central ones are the handiwork of the queen; the outer rings were produced by workers of the colony.

180

During her hurried labors of early days, the queen stops at flowers for occasional quick draughts of nourishing nectar. It is on such fare mainly that she lives. The fierce hunting instinct, which sends her ranging over the countryside in search of living prey, stirs into activity only with the development of the larvae within their cells. After their initial sip of nectar, these larvae become ravenous for animal food. The queen, and later the workers, bring in cabbage worms and other insect victims which are masticated and fed to the larvae a little at a time. In the process, the adult wasps, no doubt, swallow some of the nourishing animal fluids thus supplementing their nectar diet. Through this activity, in which they destroy great numbers of insect pests, the *Polistes* and other social wasps rank as valuable friends of the gardener.

The larvae of the wasp nest are grublike creatures, white and almost formless. When they hatch, they remain attached by their tails to the side of the cell. This prevents their falling out. Later, as they grow larger, ridges on the sides of their bodies press against the walls of the cells and hold them in place. In addition to the masticated meat which they are fed, the larvae receive frequent drinks of water. Oftentimes, a number of *Polistes* wasps can be seen bending down at the edge of a pool or puddle, imbibing long draughts for carrying back to the nest.

As soon as the first maturing worker wasp appears from the central cell, she begins helping the queen in caring for the other larvae. The eggs are laid in concentric circles out from the center. Consequently the growth of the larvae spreads evenly outward from the center to the rim and the weight is always equally balanced. This prevents an unequal strain being placed on the central stem which supports the pendant nest. Incidentally, the factor of safety of this supporting stem is very great. I once tested the strength of one stem by pulling an empty nest away and measuring the pull required. It was more than a score of times the weight of the nest itself. Even when the nests are attached to the limbs of trees, or are placed in other exposed positions, as they sometimes are, they frequently weather the gales of winter without breaking away from their supports.

The days of the larvae are spent in eating and drinking and growing. When they have reached full size, each spins a silken covering over the open end of the cell. Hidden within these capped cells, the larvae transform into the adult wasps. All of the adults which break from these paper-and-silk transformation chambers during the early weeks of summer are sexually immature females, the worker wasps of the colony. They do most of the labor of the insect city. But only the queen can lay the eggs.

I remember an instance, reported by Oliver P. Medsger, in which a nest of *Polistes* wasps was destroyed by means of chloroform-soaked cotton batting. Half a dozen of the workers escaped. A foot or so from the original site, they began the construction of a new nest. It increased in size until it was fully three inches across. But every cell was empty. The workers could build the nest; they could make the stem and the six-sided cells. But only the queen could add the eggs. Eventually, the workers stopped adding cells to this queenless nest although, for weeks afterwards, they wandered over it, searching for the hatching larvae which never appeared.

During the hottest days of summer, *Polistes* workers regulate the temperature of the brood cells by fanning their wings like honeybees to set up cooling currents of air. Sometimes they do even more. Part of the water which they transport to the nest, on such days, is employed in temperature control. It is used to saturate parts of the paper; by its evaporation, it lowers the excessive temperature.

The *Polistes* are, in the main, peaceable wasps. Their fiery stings are to be respected but they use them only as a last resort, when seriously molested. They do not employ them to paralyze prey as does the cicada-killer, nor do they use them in such swift retribution as is meted out by a disturbed colony of yellow-jackets. They are intent upon their own business and do not go out of their way to meet trouble.

In this business, they range far over the countryside. But always they wing their way back to the nest where they were born. Phil

182

Rau, and others, have demonstrated that eyesight guides them home. In one experiment, Rau took half a dozen queens from their nests and carried them in complete darkness through a wheat field, a corn patch, a strip of dense woods. Released beyond the woods, the wasps flew home in from twenty-two to seventy-two minutes.

At the time they were set free, the queens darted this way and that. The spot seemed new to them. But eventually each insect found some landmark that was familiar and from then on the road was easy. The wasps apparently fly from landmark to landmark. When Rau liberated wasps with their antennae mutilated, they found their way home just the same. The secret of their ability lay in their eyes, not in their smelling antennae. Anyone who is interested in further researches in the field of the habits and homing abilities of the wasps will find engrossing pages in the Raus' *Wasp Studies Afield*. This entomological classic was published in 1918 by the Princeton University Press.

Although the antennae are not used by the insects to find their way home, they are employed for many other things. One of these is telling the difference between a drop of nectar and a drop of dew. The wasps accomplish this with their feelers. In an instant, they can distinguish between plain and sweetened water. If acid or quinine is added to sweetened water, the fact is apparently detected by the insect's antennae. They promptly ignore the fluid. Among the flowers, *Polistes* wasps can differentiate between nectar and raindrops with a minimum loss of time.

In the waning days of summer, the population of the wasp's insect city reaches its peak. The nest now may measure as much as half a foot across. From some of the latter cells come a new type of individual. This wasp can be recognized in an instant by its white face. It is the male. Up until now only the fertile queen, or queens, and the sexually immature female workers have made up the population of the nest. The males, which fly about on autumn days, have no stings. I have seen an entomologist who knew his wasps amaze a group by catching males, until he had a dozen or

183

more, and then suddenly opening his hand to permit the harmless, nonstinging insects to escape.

About the time that some cells are giving forth the light-faced males, others are producing the true females, the virgin queens with which they mate. This is the climaxing event in the annals of the wasp-cities. A change comes over the workers. As autumn advances, there is a reversal of their instinct of solicitude for the larvae. The young wasps in the cells can never mature before the coming of cold. The workers, sensing this, cease to bring in food. More than this, they often fall upon the helpless brood and destroy it—the same brood which, during summer months, they would defend with their lives if necessary.

Food grows more scarce as fall approaches winter. The last flowers of the season are combed for drops of nectar. During their final days, the workers subsist largely on the juices of fallen fruit. As the chill of the evening grows more severe, the wasps huddle on or about the nest, numbed and motionless. Well into November I have sometimes seen workers still clinging to the empty nest. With their feet thrust straight backward, a few crawl head-first into the cells for greater protection. But, by then, life has gone out of the once-populous city. The last of the dulled workers perishes in the first hard freeze.

The queens, which have mated with the males, alone survive. Within their bodies lie the whole populations of the wasp-nests of another season. Safely secreted away in crannies and cracks, beneath old rubbish and in other hiding places, they pass the long winter hibernation. On the coldest days, they cling as though dead, reviving and moving about, or even making short flights, during winter thaws. Such flights form one of the greatest dangers to the overwintering queens. Lured out of a carefully chosen and safe retreat by the warm weather of midday, they are soon affected by the chill of the advancing afternoon and hurriedly seek shelter. These on-the-spur-of-the-moment hiding places are less safe and satisfactory. In them, the wasps are more likely to be found by rodents or overcome by adverse weather conditions. This is the

184

reason that a variable winter, in which mild spells alternate with hard freezes, is more likely to prove disastrous to the wasps than is a winter of steady cold.

During the cold months of a recent winter, I observed *Polistes* queens which were hibernating in a box of trash beside a pile of discarded timbers. Thirty-two of the insects took refuge in this one box. On the coldest days, they drew together into tightly compressed knots or clusters. One winter morning, I thought I detected white-faced males among the hibernating insects. Closer inspection, however, revealed that the white faces were produced by crystals of frost.

These particular queens were hibernating within a few feet of the nest in which they had been born. On other occasions, *Polistes* wasps often fly for considerable distances to find a hibernaculum to their liking. Among the trees of a lowland along the Mississippi River, south of St. Louis, Phil Rau found the nests of thousands of *Polistes annularis*. Each year, as autumn came, the young queens of these insects deserted their summer grounds and traveled five miles to the Cliff Cave region where they hibernated in crevices among the rocks. In the spring, they flew back again to the trees of the lowland.

Of course, spring comes too late for many of the queens. A large number of them fail to survive. Mice devour some; the cold kills others; while still others lack the vitality to endure the long strain. The mortality among the hibernating insects is often great, depending largely upon the weather conditions that prevail in winter months. From year to year, the number of *Polistes* nests varies greatly in a given region—varies according to the fortunes of the overwintering queens. For each insect-city has its beginnings in a queen; she is the protagonist in the drama of its rise and fall.

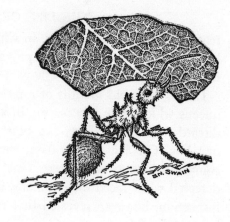

14. THE LIFE OF
THE ANT

BENJAMIN FRANKLIN considered the ant the ideal of moralists. "None," he wrote, "preaches better than the ant and she says nothing." King Solomon thought of the ant as the symbol of wisdom. "Consider her ways," he said, "and be wise." Charles Darwin concluded that the ant is "the most marvelous atom in the world, except the human brain." In all ages, men of action and men of reflection have been fascinated by the busy, efficient, enigmatic life of the anthill.

No other insect except the honeybee has attained a more complex social order. No other insect has developed more varied means of livelihood. No other insect has been more successful in survival and expansion. Ant colonies are found from mountaintops to swamplands around the world. And, as the great American formicologist, Dr. William Morton Wheeler, of Harvard, pointed out, the ants outnumber in individuals all other terrestrial animals.

186

Their great underground cities, in which the worker ants sometimes live for as long as seven years and the queens for as long as fifteen, have a stability virtually unknown among other insects. An anthill may outlast a human generation.

This vast colony is held together by what H. G. Wells has called "the patriotism of smell." All the ants of a group have the same odor. Friend is recognized from foe by the sense of smell. The olfactory organs of its antennae are so vital to the ant that the insect is lost if its feelers are amputated. Among all these insects-of-the-same-smell, the duties of the day are efficiently apportioned. Some depart on foraging expeditions; others clean house; others remain in the nurseries to care for the young ants. Within a given community, there is harmony and mutual aid.

Three different types of individuals make up these communities. They are the queens, the males, and the workers, or neuters. These latter insects are vastly in the majority. They are wingless and sexually immature. Far more than nine-tenths of all the ants you see are devoid of wings. Only at the time of the mating and dispersal flights, do the winged males and the winged true females appear. They establish new colonies, thus spreading the species. The wings on which they ride are membranous and four in number—like the wings of the bees and wasps. They identify the ants with the *Hymenoptera* order.

The flying honeymoon of these insects, the great exodus of the winged individuals, marks the beginning of a cycle in the history of an ant-city. Thousands of new nests are established as a consequence of this flight. Sometimes, I have seen the air filled with the glinting forms of flying ants for miles on end. For their exodus, the winged insects choose an hour of calm and clear skies—often following a day of rain. As though at some silent signal, the ants often arise simultaneously from a thousand nests and spread away over many square miles of countryside. Millions of ants sail on the calm air of late afternoon. Like the swarming of the honeybees, the dispersal flight of the winged ants is the great dramatic event in the laborious life of the colony.

The wings of the ant are used but once. Upon alighting, the queens break off their wings, either with their legs and jaws or by rubbing them against grassblades. The male never uses his again because he dies soon after alighting. The fertilized female then digs her way into the ground. Henceforth, the queens will be prisoners within their subterranean caverns. Like the queen honeybees, they do no foraging. Their life-work is the laying of the eggs. In the anthill, there may be a number of queens laying eggs at the same time, as opposed to the honeybee colony in which a single queen is the rule.

The powerful wing muscles which fill the thorax of the queen ants, and which propelled them through the air, are henceforth useless. Research scientists have found that they degenerate and disappear, being absorbed into the bloodstream in the form of fatty and albuminoid substances and carried to the ovaries where they contribute to the growth of the eggs. Within a few weeks after the queen digs her way into the earth, the great flight muscles of her body have disappeared completely.

Much still remains to be learned about the events which immediately follow the termination of the dispersal flight; the latter chapters in the story of the ant nest are better known than the initial ones. However, it is certain that the earliest eggs laid at the site of the new insect-city produce nothing but workers. In the same anthill some of the workers are larger than others. The largest ants in the colony are called "majors," the smaller ones, "minors." The explanation of this difference in size seems to be that some of the ants receive more food when they are growing up than others do. This same result is noticed among bumblebees. In the latter case, the small bumblebees were the first produced in the nest. They matured at a time when the queen had to do all the work and was unable to supply them with as much food as the larvae received later on when there were many worker bees to help. The first children of a new anthill are fed only on the saliva of the queen. In some cases, the most minute of the workers are less than a hundredth the bulk of the queen.

188

Each ant, no matter what its size or sex or species, goes through four distinct stages in reaching its maturity. Like the butterfly and the wasp, its metamorphosis is complete. From the egg issues forth a soft, legless grub. It is shaped like a crook-necked gourd, is whitish and translucent. It consists of a head and thirteen segments, the head being at the smaller end of the larva. As soon as it appears, the nurse-ants take it in charge.

Even before that, they have been guarding and caring for the egg from which it came. At intervals, they have carefully licked the surface of the egg—a process which is believed to prevent the formation of mold. The saliva also causes several of the half-millimeter-long eggs to stick together in a packet which can be carried away more easily in a time of danger.

In feeding the larvae the workers of different species employ varying procedures. Some of them feed the grubs only regurgitated liquids; others give them nothing but solid fare; still others feed them both. Carnivorous ants offer their larvae parts of insects and harvester ants nourish theirs on fragments of seeds. In addition to bringing regular and frequent meals to the nurseries of the colony, the workers clean the larvae and transport them from place to place to take advantage of changes in temperature and humidity within the soil.

It is when the larvae reach their full growth and are ready to transform into pupae that one of the most amazing of all the surprising events of the anthill takes place. In cocoon-spinning species, the nurse-ants dig little cavities in the ground and place the larvae in them. The young ant has to lie in just such a depression in order to produce the elliptical envelope of silk with which it surrounds itself. It cannot produce its cocoon otherwise. It has to attach the threads of silk, which come from glands that end in its mouth, to the walls of an excavated chamber. Moving its head back and forth, it lines the depression, and surrounds itself, with a fine web of silk. As soon as the worker ants see that this cocoon has been completed, they dig up the transforming larva and carefully clean the outside of the silken envelope of all adhering particles of dirt.

In both shape and color the cocoons of different species have individual variations. Some are long and slender, some are elliptical, some are oblong; some are dark brown, some pale buff, and others sulphur yellow. The cocoons are carefully stored in a different part of the nest from the spot where the eggs are kept. In time of danger, the workers carry both eggs and cocoons to a place of safety. The nurseries are the treasure vaults of the anthill. Incidentally, it is the cocoons which are sold commercially as "ant eggs" for feeding goldfish and not the real eggs of the insects.

In those great wars which sometimes take place between rival colonies, the pupae of the attacked ants form the booty of the conflict. "The ants' most dangerous enemies," says Forel, "are other ants, just as man's most dangerous enemies are other men." Anyone who has read Henry D. Thoreau's *Walden* will remember his classic description of the silent fury with which a war of the ants raged, hour after hour amid the chips beside his cabin.

"The legions of these Myrmidons," he tells us, "covered all the hills and vales of my woodyard. The ground was already strewn with the dead and dying, both red and black. On every side they were engaged in deadly combat. . . . I watched a couple that were fast locked in each other's embraces, in a little sunny valley amid the chips, now at noonday prepared to fight until the sun went down, or life went out. . . . I never learned which party was victorious, nor the cause of the war; but I felt the rest of the day as if I had had my feelings excited and harrowed by witnessing the struggle, the ferocity and carnage, of a human battle before my door."

Thoreau's record, probably the most widely read account of an ant war ever written, gives a vivid picture of the savagery of such a conflict. Almost always the black ants are the attacked instead of the attackers. The smaller red ants fall upon them in an effort to rob them of the maturing pupae within the nest. When they are successful, the red invaders troop home laden with the cocoons of the black ants. The insects which appear from these cocoons

190

become the slaves of their captors. In some instances, for so many generations have certain ants been waited upon by slaves obtained in this way that they have lost the power of feeding and caring for themselves.

Under normal conditions, where the ants mature within nests of their own kind, they spend from thirteen to twenty-two days as pupae. Hidden within their silken envelopes, they transform into adults ready to take up the duties of the colony. The nurses, watching over the cocoons, bite open the ends and thus aid the newly emerging adults to escape. From then on, the life and duties of the ant depend upon its species.

If it is one of the black carpenter ants, its days will be spent in and around some fallen decaying log or old tree or in the heartwood of a living tree. If it is one of the harvester ants, it will range far and wide collecting seeds. If it is one of the agricultural ants of the Southwest, it will bring in bits of leaves and form subterranean fungus-gardens where it will raise and harvest its own crops. If it is a honey-ant of the desert regions, it will collect the sweet fluid of aphides and store it in the bodies of special members of the colony whose distended abdomens form living jars or casks. If it is the most common and widespread of American species, the familiar red garden ant, it will search endlessly for a vast variety of foods that range from sweet honeydew to the bodies of dead crickets and other insects.

And each of these activities requires specialized, and often surprising, abilities. Harvester ants, that store quantities of seeds underground, nip the radicle from each seed to keep the grain from sprouting. After a drenching rain, they transport the seeds to the surface and spread them out in the sunshine to check the formation of mold. Fungus-growing ants are known to fertilize their underground gardens with their own excrement in order to increase the crop from their tiny fields. Ants that tend plant lice, and milk them regularly of their honeydew, sometimes build "barns" to shelter their insect cattle. One species of ant often found on dogwood employs a mortar of earth and vegetable matter for

191

this purpose. Within such shelters, the aphides can feed without being disturbed by their enemies.

The celebrated Swiss student of the ants, Auguste Forel, once watched a large colony of ants foraging for dead insects. He discovered that they were bringing them in at the rate of twenty-eight a minute. He estimated that this one colony gathered in as many as 100,000 small insect bodies in the course of an active day. Hunting ants of this kind often show remarkable ability in adjusting the number of workers to the size of the load that has to be transported.

A striking instance of the kind is given by R. W. G. Hingston in his volume, *Instinct and Intelligence*. Cutting up a dead grasshopper into three unequal parts, he dropped them where the foraging ants of a colony would discover them. The second piece was twice the size of the first and the third was twice the size of the second. At the end of forty minutes, Hingston counted the number of workers that had been dispatched to each piece. There were twenty-eight at the smallest fragment, forty-four at the middle-sized one, and eighty-nine at the largest. These numbers are roughly in the same proportions as the sizes of the insect-pieces the ants had to pull back to the nest.

An interesting parallel between the social evolution of ants and men has been noted by several scientists. The earliest men were hunters; later they became pastoral, following their flocks about; and finally they settled down to cultivating the soil and became agriculturists. In like manner, the ants seem to have progressed. The most primitive species were the roving hunters. Later types began the long association between ants and aphides; they were the pastoral species. And then, in turn, came the fungus-growing ants, the counterpart of the farmers among men.

All of these ants have one curious habit in common. The insects are said to have a "social stomach." They share their food with their neighbors. In one instance, an experimenter fed an ant, of a species which has an almost transparent section in its abdomen, honey which had been dyed a brilliant blue. Within a few hours, dozens of ants in the colony were walking around with their abdomens tinged with blue. They all had obtained drops of food from the original ant or from one of those that had solicited food from it. When an ant swallows food, only part of it goes to its stomach. The rest is retained for the time being in a sort of crop from which it can bring up small quantities to feed other members of the colony. I have seen an ant stop in the midst of her aphid-milking to present drops of regurgitated honeydew to four workers which passed by in quick succession.

In connection with the feeding habits of ants, scientists have demonstrated that these small insects carry within their bodies a kind of living alarm clock. When captive ants are fed at, say, ten o'clock in the morning and three o'clock in the afternoon, they learn to come at those hours. After a period of training, a given lapse of time seems impressed upon their nervous systems. That these "clocks" are within their bodies and dependent upon their life-processes is conclusively demonstrated by a simple experiment. When the insects are given drugs that slow down or speed up their activity, they appear to lose track of time. They come either too late or too early for the feeding. The chemicals have thrown their "nervous-system clocks" out of order.

In spite of the amazing capacities of the ants, and their cooperative achievements, they have little ability for improvising. They can learn by trial and error. But they cannot solve problems in advance. A chimpanzee will pile boxes one on top of another in order to reach bananas suspended from the ceiling of its cage. But, as John Lubbock, the English statesman whose spare-time studies of ants made him one of the world's pioneer formicologists, learned, ants cannot reason sufficiently to build a mound only one-eighth of an inch high in order to reach honey that they can see and smell and upon which the lives of themselves and their offspring depends. In the main, the ant is the triumph of instinctive behavior.

Throughout the summer, its instincts keep it laboring such long hours and so incessantly that it has become, in the popular mind, a symbol for industry. But, like that other symbol for diligence, the

193

beaver, it catches up on its sleep, in northern states, when winter comes. Then it has a rest that extends for months on end. When the autumn rains, frosts, and booming winds give place to winter's steady cold, the ant multitudes mass together in their underground caverns for their weeks of hibernation. There they remain until spring brings them into the open again for another period of intense and effective labor.

Thus the life of the ant has proceeded for untold ages. In form and habits those of today differ but little from those that have lain buried in Baltic amber since the Oligocene Period. The instincts of the ants have welded them together into an efficient and lasting social order that has withstood eons of continual change. Their cities antedate Pekin and Rome by millions of years. Their social communities are among the oldest "civilizations" on earth.

During these long stretches of time, the habits of the ants have virtually stood still. They have continued the same complex way of life millennium after millennium. It is a way of life so successful that little variation is needed.

Summing up his impression of these insects, which he had studied so assiduously for so many years, John Lubbock, in 1881, expressed an opinion with which many subsequent students have been in accord. "When we consider the habits of ants," Lubbock wrote, "their social organization, their large communities, and elaborate habitations; their roadways, their possession of domestic animals, and even, in some cases, of slaves, it must be admitted that they have a fair claim to rank next to man in the scale of intelligence."

BIBLIOGRAPHY

BIBLIOGRAPHY

American Social Insects, by Charles D. Michener and Mary H. Michener. Van Nostrand, 1951.

Ants, by William Morton Wheeler. Columbia University Press, 1926.

Bee Keeping, by Everett F. Phillips. Macmillan, 1918.

Bees, Their Vision, Chemical Senses and Language, by Karl Von Frisch. Cornell University Press, 1953.

Biology of Dragonflies, The, by R. J. Tillyard. Cambridge University Press, 1917.

Biology of Mayflies With a Systematic Account of North American Species, by J. G. Needham, J. R. Traver and Y. H. Hsu. Comstock, 1935.

Bramble-Bees and Others, by J. Henri Fabre. Dodd, Mead, 1915.

Bumblebees and Their Ways, by Otto E. Plath. Macmillan, 1934.

Butterfly Book, The, by W. J. Holland. Doubleday, 1916.

Butterflies of the District of Columbia and Vicinity, The, by Austin H. Clark. Smithsonian Institution. U.S. National Museum Bulletin 157, 1932.

Butterflies of North America, The, by W. H. Edwards. Houghton, Mifflin, 1897.

College Entomology, by E. O. Essig. Macmillan, 1951.

Dancing Bees, The, by Karl Von Frisch. Harcourt, Brace, 1953.

Destructive and Useful Insects, by C. L. Metcalf and W. P. Flint. McGraw-Hill, 1951.

Everyday Doings of Insects, by Evelyn Cheesman. McBride, 1927.

Fieldbook of Animals in Winter, by Ann Haven Morgan. Putnam, 1939.

Fieldbook of Insects, by Frank E. Lutz. Putnam, 1948.

Fieldbook of Ponds and Streams, by Ann Haven Morgan. Putnam, 1930.

Fieldbook of Natural History, by E. L. Palmer. McGraw-Hill, 1949.

197

BIBLIOGRAPHY

Field Guide to the Butterflies, A, by Alexander B. Klots. Houghton, Mifflin, 1951.

Gardener's Bug Book, The, by C. Wescott. Doubleday, 1946.

General Entomology, by S. W. Frost. McGraw-Hill, 1942.

General Textbook of Entomology, A, by A. D. Imms. Wiley, 1957.

Golden Throng, The, by Edwin Way Teale. Dodd, Mead, 1961.

Grasshopper Book, The, by Wilfrid S. Bronson. Harcourt, Brace, 1943.

Grassroot Jungles, by Edwin Way Teale. Dodd, Mead, 1944.

Handbook of the Dragonflies of North America, A, by J. G. Needham and H. B. Heywood. Thomas, 1929.

Handbook of Nature Study, by Anna Botsford Comstock. Comstock, 1911.

Handbook of the Mosquitoes of North America, by R. Matheson. Comstock, 1944.

Hive and the Honeybee, The, by Roy A. Grout. Dadant, 1946.

How Insects Live, by Walter H. Wellhouse. Macmillan, 1926.

How to Know the Butterflies, by J. H. Comstock and A. B. Comstock. Appleton, 1904.

Hunting Wasps, The, by J. Henri Fabre. Dodd, Mead, 1915.

Insect Adventures, by J. Henri Fabre. Dodd, Mead, 1929.

Insect Book, The, by Leland O. Howard. Doubleday, 1923.

Insect Dietary, by C. T. Brues. Harvard, 1946.

Insect Fact and Folklore, by Lucy W. Clausen. Macmillan, 1954.

Insect Friends, by Edwin Way Teale. Dodd, Mead, 1955.

Insect Guide, The, by Ralph B. Swain. Doubleday, 1948.

Insect Invaders, by Anthony Standen. Houghton, Mifflin, 1943.

Insect World of J. Henri Fabre, The, by J. Henri Fabre. Edited by Edwin Way Teale. Dodd, Mead, 1949.

Insects, by Herbert S. Zim and Clarence Cottam. Simon and Schuster, 1951.

Insects, U.S. Department of Agriculture. Yearbook of Agriculture, 1952.

Insects in Their World, by Su Zan N. Swain. Garden City, 1955.

Instinct and Intelligence, by R. W. G. Hingston. Macmillan, 1929.

Introducing the Insects, by F. A. Urquhart. Holt, 1949.

Introduction to Entomology, An, by J. H. Comstock. Comstock, 1960.

Introduction to the Study of Insects, An, by Donald J. Borror and D. M. DeLong. Rinehart, 1957.

Junior Book of Insects, The, by Edwin Way Teale. Dutton, 1953.

Leaf-Mining Insects, by J. G. Needham and others. Williams and Williams, 1928.

Life of the Bee, The, by Maurice Maeterlinck. Dodd, Mead, 1901.

Life of the Caterpillar, The, by J. Henri Fabre. Dodd, Mead, 1918.

Life of the Fly, The, by J. Henri Fabre. Dodd, Mead, 1913.

Life of the Grasshopper, The, by J. Henri Fabre. Dodd, Mead, 1917.

Life of Inland Waters, The, by J. G. Needham and J. T. Lloyd. Comstock, 1937.

Life of the Weevil, The, by J. Henri Fabre. Dodd, Mead, 1922.
Living Insects of the World, by A. B. Klots and Elsie B. Klots. Doubleday, 1959.
Lot of Insects, A, by Frank E. Lutz. Putnam, 1941.
Marvels of Insect Life, by Edward Step. McBride, 1938.
Mason-Bees, The, by J. Henri Fabre. Dodd, Mead, 1914.
Mason-Wasps, The, by J. Henri Fabre. Dodd, Mead, 1919.
Moth Book, The, by W. J. Holland. Doubleday, 1934.
Moths, by E. B. Ford. Macmillan, 1955.
Natural History of Aquatic Insects, The, by L. C. Miall. Macmillan, 1934.
Natural History of Mosquitoes, The, by Marston Bates. Macmillan, 1949.
Near Horizons; The Story of an Insect Garden, by Edwin Way Teale. Dodd, Mead, 1942.
Of Ants and Men, by C. P. Haskins. Prentice-Hall, 1939.
1001 Questions Answered About Insects, by A. B. Klots and Elsie B. Klots. Dodd, Mead, 1961.
Orthoptera of Northeastern America, by W. S. Blatchley. Nature Pub. Co., 1920.
Our Enemy the Termite, by Thomas E. Snyder. Comstock, 1935.
Our Insect Friends and Foes, by William Atherton DyPuy. Winston, 1935.
Our Insect Friends and Foes and Spiders. National Geographic Society, 1935.
Outlines of Entomology, by A. D. Imms. Dutton, 1942.
Plant Galls and Gall Makers, by E. P. Felt. Williams and Williams, 1928.
Principles of Insect Morphology, by R. E. Snodgrass. McGraw-Hill, 1935.
Principles of Insect Physiology, The, by V. B. Wigglesworth. Dutton, 1956.
Psychic Life of Insects, The, by Eugene L. Bovier. Appleton, 1922.
Sacred Bee, The, by Hilda M. Ransome. Houghton, Mifflin, 1937.
Sacred Beetle and Others, The, by J. Henri Fabre. Dodd, Mead, 1924.
Social Insects, The, by William Morton Wheeler. Harcourt, Brace, 1928.
Wasp Studies Afield, by Phil Rau and Nellie Rau. Princeton, 1918.
Wonderful World of Insects, The, by Albro T. Gaul. Rinehart, 1953.
World of Butterflies and Moths, The, by A. B. Klots. McGraw-Hill, 1959.

INDEX

INDEX

Achrioptera spinossissima 6
Aeschna 42
Alder flies 38
"Alpine rock crawler" 20
Ambush bugs 9, 30, 130
Anax junius 48
Ant lions 10, 30, 132, 138
Ants 3, 7-8, 10-11, 12, 19, 21, 22,
    29, 30, 31, 33, 34, 37, 40, 43-
    44, 45, 46, 47, 48, 52, 89, 93,
    104, 114, 119-20, 133, 167,
    171, 177, 178, 186-94
  army 11
  black 190
  carpenter 87, 90, 191
  fire 11
  flying 41
  harvester 191
  honey 10-11
  red 190, 191
  slave-making 11, 194
  tree 11
Aphides 9, 23, 28, 53, 109-20, 132,
    133-37, 164-65, 168, 171, 191,
    192, 193
  apple 119
  cherry 115
  corn-root 119-20

  grape 113, 118
  hop 112, 116, 118
  pea 113
  rose 117
Aphis-lions 9, 134-37, 165
Aphis maidi-radicis 119
Aphis-wolves 164, 165
Apis mellifera 55
Apple aphides 119
Assassin bugs 130, 166

Backswimmers 67, 129
Bates, Henry W. 11
Bedbugs 130
Beebe, William 5
Bees 3, 7, 19, 21, 24, 26, 29, 33, 34,
    36, 37, 38, 39, 41, 42, 43, 44,
    45-46, 51, 52, 55-56, 88, 93,
    131, 156, 171, 177, 178, 182,
    186, 187, 188
  leafcutter 177
Beetles 4, 7, 8, 9, 11, 20, 21, 22, 24,
    26, 27, 28-29, 32, 36, 41, 42,
    49, 52, 102, 128, 131, 137, 169
  bark 36
  blister 8, 169
  bombardier 9, 30
  carrion 29, 169

Beetles (*continued*)
  cerambycid 11
  click 169
  Colorado potato 32, 57, 165
  deathwatch 12, 45
  diving 36, 37, 40, 67, 169
  drugstore 11
  Hercules 9
  Japanese 58
  ladybird 30, 42, 58, 112, 162-69
  long-horned 169
  May 23, 33, 54, 169
  scarab 22, 169
  spotted bean 163
  stag 169
  tiger 29, 31, 32, 169
  water 30, 77
  whirligig 40
  wood 10
  wood-boring 32
Beutenmüller, William 80
Bird-lice 59
Birth, of insects 23-25
Blissus leucopterus 122
Boll weevils 57-58, 169
Bonnet (French scientist) 116
Book-lice 59
Botflies 25, 43, 161
Brachinus fumans 9
Brancsikia aeroplana 5
Breathing, by insects 37
Bristletails 59
Bronson, Wilfrid 99
Brownie bugs 120
Bumblebees 9, 26, 27, 31, 39, 41, 42, 47, 51, 54, 102, 161, 178, 188
Butterflies 3, 8, 10, 12, 19, 20, 24, 26, 28, 29, 30-31, 34, 35, 36, 41, 42, 44, 49, 52, 105, 151, 171, 177, 189
  anglewing 140
  cabbage 32
  dead-leaf 5

  fritillary 140, 151
  monarch 9, 23, 30, 31, 36, 39, 44, 53, 54, 59, 139-51
  morpho 32
  mourning cloak 34, 36, 54, 140, 149
  red admiral 36
  swallowtail 30, 54, 103, 105, 145, 151
  "thaw" 140
  viceroy 31, 54, 145-46
  wanderer 112

Caddis-fly 132
Carpenter, Frank M. 17
Caterpillars 25, 26, 27, 28, 30, 31, 32, 34, 36, 38, 48, 52, 59, 102, 106, 112, 142, 146, 161
  gypsy moth 151
  monarch 141-43
  tent 54
  viceroy 145
  woolly-bear 54
Cecidomyiidae 25
Cephenemyia pratti 43
Cercopidae 7
Cherry aphides 115
Chinch bugs 25, 54, 57, 58, 121-30
Chitin 26-27, 31
Cicadas 11-12, 25, 27, 35, 40, 43, 53, 120, 170-77
Circulation system, of insects 37-39
Cluster-flies 50
Cockroaches 19, 28, 34, 38, 47, 50, 100
Coleoptera, see Beetles, ladybird
Color, of insects 31-32
Communication, by insects 45-46
Comstock, John Henry 59
Conniption bugs 138
Corn borers 57, 58
Corn-root aphides 119-20
Corrodentia 59
Craneflies 43, 160

Crevecoeur, Hector St. John de 159
Crickets 22, 25, 28, 34, 35, 36, 40,
    53, 54, 94-100, 108
    snowy tree 48-49, 100

Daddylonglegs 18, 112
Damselflies 41, 54, 76, 138
Darwin, Charles 6, 186
Davis, William T. 80
Death, of insects 55-56
Dermatobia hominis 25
Dickens, Charles 100
Diopsis apicalis 10
Diptera 25
Diptera, see Flies, house
Dobson flies 24, 138
Doodle bugs 138
Dorsey, George A. 49
Dragonflies 10, 17, 19, 23, 25, 28,
    29, 31, 33, 34, 39, 40, 41, 42,
    43, 44, 47, 48, 49, 52, 54, 67,
    71, 74-84, 87, 103, 131
Drosophila melanogaster 161

Ears, of insects 34-35
Earthworms 18
Eating habits, of insects 28-30
Electric light bugs 130
Ellzey, M. G. 148
Emerson, Alfred E. 89
Enemies, avoidance of, by insects 30-
    31
Ephemeroptera, see Flies, May
Erebus 19
Eristalis tenax 37, 42
Essig, E. O. 59
Euchirus longimanus 10
Eumicrosoma benefica 128
Eyes, of insects 32-33

Fabre, J. Henri 7, 51, 106
Feeling, of insects 35
Fireflies 45, 131, 169
Flies 12, 21, 24, 25, 26, 28, 33, 34,
    36, 46, 53, 55, 171

alder 138
antelope 160
antlered 10
big-headed 161
black 40, 160
caddie 29
chalcid 24, 112
dance 161
deer 160
dobson 24, 138
fairy 10, 83, 177
flesh 161
flower 112
fruit 36, 53, 161
Hessian 25, 57, 58, 161
house 23, 36, 38, 42, 103, 152-61
hover 161
hump-backed 161
ichneumon 25, 30, 34, 52, 131,
    177
lacewing 23, 30, 41, 43, 54, 112,
    131-38, 165
lantern 120
May 27, 40, 41, 53, 54, 119
peacock 161
robber 9, 29, 30, 31, 33, 41, 47,
    48, 161
stalk-eyed 10
stiletto 161
Syrphid 37
Flight, by insects 40-43
Flint, W. P. 111
Food, of insects 28-30
Forel, Auguste 190, 192
Fossil insects 17-18, 65, 87
Franklin, Benjamin 73, 186
Froghoppers 7, 120
Frost, S. W. 32, 117
Fungine 26

Gnats 34, 35, 160
Goethe 73
Grape aphides 113, 118

Grasshoppers 4-5, 12, 19, 23, 25, 28, 34, 35, 37, 40, 42, 47, 49, 53, 54, 100, 105, 171, 192
Growth, of insects 26-28
Grylloblatta campodeiformis 20

Hearing, of insects 34-35
Hellgrammites 138
Hemiptera 24
Hemiptera, see Chinch bugs
Hingston, R. W. G. 167, 192
Homoptera, see Aphides
Honeybees, *see* Bees
Hop aphides 112, 116, 118
Hornets 102, 104, 159
House flies 23, 36, 38, 42, 103, 152-61
Housefly, *see* Flies
Howard, Leland O. 57, 80, 83, 156, 158, 160
Hudson, W. H. 81
Huxley, Thomas 112
Hymenoptera 21, 41, 59
Hymenoptera, see Ants; Bees; Wasps

"Ice bug" 20
Instar 26
Instinct, insects and 50-52
Isoptera, see Termites

Joel 57
Junebugs 169

Kallima 5
Kallima inachis 5
Katydids 5, 28, 31, 34, 35, 53, 55, 100
Kirby, William 12
Klots, Elsie B. 77

Lace bugs 130
Ladybugs, *see* Beetles, ladybird
Langmuir, Irving 43

Lantern flies 120
Leaf hoppers 120
Leaf-miners 28
Legs, of insects 39-40
Lepidoptera 28, 59
Lepidoptera, see Butterflies, monarch
Lice 153
  plant 9, 19, 24, 54, 105, 109-20, 134-37, 163, 164, 165, 168, 191
Life cycles, of insects 53
Light changes, response of insects to 49-50
Linnaeus, Carl 114
Liphyra brassolis 8
Location, sense of, in insects 43-44
Locusts 3, 30, 34, 35, 37, 40, 49, 57
Lubbock, John 193, 194
Lutz, Frank E. 53, 96, 97, 150

Maeterlinck, Maurice 23, 56
Maggots
  rat-tailed 6-7, 30, 37
Malacosoma americana 54
Mallophaga 59
Mann, William M. 11
Mantises, *see* Praying mantises
Marsh-measurers 130
Mealy bugs 120
Medsger, Oliver P. 182
Megarhyssa lunator 30, 34, 177
Membracidae 6
Memory, of insects 46-47, 167
Metaprosagoga insignis 4
Metcalf, C. L. 111
Miall, L. C. 12
Miaster 25
Microlepidoptera 10, 151
Midges 160, 161
Migration, by insects 44-45, 147-49
Millipedes 18
Mites, red 159
Molting fluid 27
Molts 26, 27, 28

Morgan, Ann Haven 71, 160
Mosquitoes 22, 24, 25, 29, 34, 40,
    48, 54, 75, 83, 137, 152, 153,
    160, 161
Moths 10, 12, 19, 20, 24, 26, 28,
    33-34, 47, 49-50, 105, 137, 140,
    143, 144, 146, 150-51
  atlas 9
  brown 6
  Catocala 31
  Cecropia 33, 54, 150
  clearwing 151
  gold-tailed 50
  gypsy 151
  Luna 54, 150
  Polyphemus 33, 54, 150
  Promethea 54
  silk 26, 150-51
  sphinx 38, 42, 151

Needham, James G. 79
Neuroptera, see Flies, lacewing

Odonata, see Dragonflies
Oecophylla smaragdina 11
Oil-beetle 7
Orthoptera 4
Orthoptera, see Crickets; Praying
    mantises

Palophus reyi 6
Papilio troilus 30
Pea-aphides 113
Phorodon humuli 116
Phylloxera vastatrix 113
Plant lice, *see* Lice, plant
Plath, Otto 9
Pliny the Elder 3, 114-15, 141
Polistes wasps, *see* Wasps, paper-
    making
Praying mantises 4, 19, 29, 30, 35,
    40, 47, 52, 54, 80, 101-8, 112

Rau, Nellie 44, 171

Rau, Phil 44, 171, 182-83, 185
Reaumur, René A. F. 37, 64, 69, 71,
    111
Rhodnius 10, 53
Riley, C. V. 175
Roosevelt, Theodore 152
Rose aphides 117

Santos-Dumont, Alberto 83
Sawflies 34, 52, 177
Say, Thomas 122
Scorpions
  water 129
Scudder, Samuel H. 49, 144
Shapley, Harlow 48
"Short-circuit beetle" 29
Sight, of insects 32-33
Silverfish 19
Sleeping habits, of insects 47-48
Slingerland, M. V. 116, 118
Smelling, by insects 33-34
Snakes 18
"Snow fleas" 20
Sow bugs 18
Spence, William 12
Spiders 6, 18, 71, 128, 159
Springtails 20
Squash bugs 103, 130
Stink bugs 8, 130
Stoneflies 40, 67
Strepsiptera 42, 59
Swammerdam, Jan 67-68, 74
Swift, Dean 59
Swimming ability, of insects 40
Syrphus americanus 112

Taste, sense of, in insects 35-37
Telea polyphemus 26
Temperature changes, response of in-
    sects to 48-49
Tennyson, Alfred 79
Termites 11, 24, 50, 85-93
  compass 93

Therates labiatus 4
Thomson, J. Arthur 73, 110
Thoreau, Henry 49, 190
Thread-legged bugs 130
Thysanura 59
Tillyard, R. J. 43, 75
Touch, sense of, in insects 35
Treehoppers 6, 120
Tremex 34
Tumblebugs 169
Twisted-winged insects 59

Vitality, of insects 52-53
Von Frisch, Karl 44, 45

Walking, by insects 39-40
Walking sticks 6, 9, 20, 28, 55, 100
Wallace, Alfred Russel 4, 5, 10, 21
Wasps 21, 24, 29, 30, 31, 41, 42, 44,
    46, 47, 93, 104, 105, 131, 156,
    159, 177, 187, 189
cicada-killer 43, 170-78
digger 51, 171, 179
mason 52
mud-dauber 177
paper-making 17, 23, 54, 179-85
Water boatmen 130
Water bugs 130
Water scorpions 129
Water-striders 19, 39, 40, 54, 130
Webster, F. W. 128
Weed, Clarence 146
Weevils 169
Weiss, Harry B. 122
Wells, H. G. 187
Wheelbugs 24, 130
Wheeler, William Morton 8, 186
White, Gilbert 110, 115
Wings, of insects 40-43
Winter survival, by insects 54-55